LANDMARK COLLECTOR'S LIBRARY

Stationary Steam Engines of Great Britain
The National Photographic Collection
Volume 4: Wales, Cheshire & Shropshire

George Watkins

The Watkins' Collection in the National Monuments Record

This comprises the photographs and notes George Watkins made during a lifetime of study of the stationary steam engine.

The Steam Engine Record is an annotated set of around 1500 mounted prints of steam engines which Watkins examined in the field between 1930 and 1980. His notebooks contain a record of additional sites for which no photographs were taken, or which comprise written historical notes. In all almost 2000 entries were made in his notebooks. There are also albums of prints arranged by engine type. A catalogue is available.

In addition there are files of notes and other records on all aspects of historical steam technology, the cataloguing of which is in progress.

The main areas of this part of the collection are:

Records of steam engine makers.

Collection of bound trade literature.

Classified collection of data files dealing with, for example, textile mill engines, marine engines.

The collection can be inspected by appointment. Copies of photographs and other documents are readily available.

Please contact:

NMR Enquiry & Research Services
National Monuments Record Centre
Kemble Drive
Swindon
Wilts
SN2 2GZ

STATIONARY STEAM ENGINES OF GREAT BRITAIN

THE NATIONAL PHOTOGRAPHIC COLLECTION

VOLUME 4:
WALES, CHESHIRE & SHROPSHIRE

George Watkins

Landmark Publishing

Published by

LANDMARK
Publishing Ltd ● ● ●

Ashbourne Hall, Cokayne Ave
Ashbourne, Derbyshire, DE6 1EJ England
Tel: (01335) 347349 Fax: (01335) 347303
e-mail: landmark@clara.net
web site: www.landmarkpublishing.co.uk

ISBN 1 901522 61 X

© George Watkins

British Library Cataloguing in Publication Data: a catalogue
record for this book is available from the British Library.

Print: Bookcraft, Midsomer Norton, Bath
Designed by: James Allsopp
Editor: A P Woolrich
Production: C L M Porter

Front cover: Marple, Goyt Mill, SER 640
Back cover: Wallasey Dock Pumping Station, SER 469
Page 3: Hyde, Slack Mills Co (No 4 Mill), SER 605

CONTENTS

FOREWORD
by A. P. Woolrich

George Watkins (1904-1989) spent most of his working life as a heating engineer and boilerman in Bristol. Starting in the 1930s, in his spare time he made short trips throughout Britain photographing and recording stationary steam engines. In 1965, aged 61, he was appointed a research assistant at the Centre for the Study of the History of Technology at Bath University, under Dr R. A. Buchanan, and was enabled to devote all his time adding to and classifying his collection. He was still making field trips until the late 1970s, when ill-health made travelling difficult.

He was an occasional contributor to *Model Engineer*, and other periodicals and wrote important papers for the *Transactions of the Newcomen Society*. Following his appointment to Bath University he was in much demand as a lecturer and produced a series of books based on his research. These were:

The Stationary Steam Engine (1968)

The Textile Mill Engine, 2 Vol, (1970, 1971), 2ed, (1999)

Man and the Steam Engine, (1975), 2 imp (1978) (with R. A. Buchanan)

The Industrial Archaeology of the Stationary Steam Engine, (1976) (with R. A. Buchanan)

The Steam Engine in Industry 2 vol, (1978, 1979)

On his death in February 1989 his collection was gifted to the Royal Commission on the Historical Monuments of England. It may be freely consulted at English Heritage's National Record Centre at Swindon. As well as photographs the collection comprises numerous technical notes about all manner of steam engine related topics; an incomparable archive of trade catalogues, some dating from the late nineteenth century; a collection of letters from like-minded friends, of value today for the light they shed on the history of the growth of Industrial Archaeology; lecture notes and slides. His library was left to Bath University.

He would visit a site and take illustrated notes and photographs, usually around half a dozen. His notes usually contained measured sketches of the machines and also the layouts of the premises he visited. In all, he travelled over 120,000 miles and visited nearly 2,000 sites, but in approximately 10% only took written notes. He filed sets of contact prints of each visit in binders sorted by engine type and between 1965-1971 he made a selection of the best prints for Bath University staff to print to a larger format. These were drymounted on card and annotated with details from his field notebooks and today form what is known at the Steam Engine Record. It is this collection, with notes, which forms the basis of the present series of regional books.

The Steam Engine Record is filed in numerical order, but catalogues are available listing makers, engine types and locations. When the field trips were being made the historic county names still applied, but the modern catalogues in the Search Room at Swindon allow searching by new counties and metropolitan areas, such as Cleveland and Greater Manchester. In this series, however, the historical county names have been retained.

When he began his surveys, he travelled by bicycle and train, and many were to sites he could reach readily from Bristol, but he soon graduated to a series of autocycles, on which he would pack his photographic gear and his clothing. He planned his trips meticulously during the winter months, writing to mill owners to gain permission, and then during following summer (when his boiler was shut down for maintenance), having saved up all his available leave time, would then spend two or three weeks on his travels, staying in bed-and-breakfast accommodation, or, as he became more widely known, with friends. During the autumn he would write up his notes, and begin planning the following year's trip.

He was initially interested in beam engines, but soon concentrated on the textile mill engines of mostly Lancashire and Yorkshire. In this he was greatly aided by local experts such as Frank Wightman and Arthur Roberts, who were working in these areas. Later his interest included colliery winding engines, waterworks and marine engines. During the War, when he found difficulty in both travelling far and in getting permission to enter industrial sites, he investigated water-powered sites, such as the Avon Valley brass mills, near Bristol, and the Worcestershire

edge tool manufacturing sites. An area of steam technology which did not concern him was the railway locomotive, though he did record a small number of industrial locomotives and traction engines he found on his visits.

The regional distribution of the sites he visited includes most English counties and a number in Wales and Scotland. The numbers of sites he saw in the counties differ greatly, with Yorkshire, Lancashire, and the counties around Bristol predominating. This is because he had close links with other workers in those areas, and he relied on this network to learn where engines might be found. Areas where he had few contacts tended to be thinly covered.

In many counties he saw sites with a marine connection. These will be covered in Volume 10 of this series. In this context this means a steam engine which drove a vessel, whether at sea, river or canal. Also preserved marine engines. Engines at waterside features such as dockside workshops are included in the regional sequence of books.

George Watkins often photographed under near impossible conditions. Engine-room lighting was frequently indifferent, and confined space often made hard the siting of the camera for obtaining adequate perspective views. For most of the work reproduced in this series he used a tripod-mounted wooden plate camera with extension bellows which he modified to accept different lenses. In his early years he was continually experimenting with different combinations of film speeds, lenses and exposure times. Although he did even-tually own a 35mm roll film camera, he was never happy with using it, and was frequently heard to grumble about the quality of modern film stock.

He used cut film, held in a dark slide, and had the films developed by a local chemist in the centres he visited so he could go back and take another if a print failed. He overcame bad lighting by having very long exposures, so was able to appear in his own prints occasionally.

The long exposures also meant he was able to 'freeze' a slow-moving engine. He did this by shielding the lens by a hand-held card or the lens cap until the engine had reached, say, top dead centre and then removing the shield momentarily. This cumulative exposure resulted in an image of a still engine, and such was his deftness of touch and impeccable timing, that it is very hard to see any kind of shake or blemish on the photographs. He was adept at 'painting with light' - utilising hand-held electric lead-lights with which he could illuminate different parts of the engine successively.

He made copies from his negatives at home for distribution to his friends by using a simple contact-print frame and developer chemicals. There are many small sets of his prints in private hands.

The lenses he used were not bloomed to prevent 'flaring' of the image caused by extraneous light from windows or hanging light bulbs, and some of the photographs reproduced are marred by this. He made his selection of prints for the Steam Engine Record on the basis of their historical and technical importance, and not on their artistic quality.

His photographs are a unique record of the end of stationary steam power in this country, being made at a time when electrification, nationalisation and trade depression created wholesale changes in the physical structure of the industrial landscape. They are an invaluable resource to our understanding of the reality of industrial activity, and will interest, as well as the technical historian, the local historian and model-maker. It is good to know they are being published, for this in turn will focus attention on the rest of his reference collection, which deserves to be more widely known and used.

ISSES (The International Stationary Steam Engine Society) is publishing a number of volumes devoted to George Watkins and his work. The first volume was published mid-2002. It includes a biography of George Watkins, reminiscences by his friends, and copies of a number of his earlier writings, including some unpublished ones from the 1930's, and an account of the Watkins collection at Swindon,

Details and prices may be obtained from:

Mr John Cooper, 73 Coniston Way, Blossom Hill,
Bewdley, Worcestershire,
DY12 2QA
Tel: 01299 402946
Email:
John.Cooper@isses2.freeserve.co.uk
Web site: www.steamenginesociety.org

The sites are in alphabetical order of geographical location, and then site name and no attempt has been made to place them by precise grid references. As work on this series has progressed it has become plain that the locations are sometimes wrong, particularly county names. This is because George used the nearest Post town, which was sometimes in the next county. This has caused problems when allocating the entries to the books of this regional series, so work has been done closely cross checking the remaining original SER cards and revising the headings is necessary.

Each entry heading has an illustration number for this volume, the location, revised as necessary and the Steam Engine Record (SER) number. This latter number is the key for accessing the copies of the field notebooks and the files of additional photographs in the National Monuments Record at Swindon.

The remaining page comprises brief illustrated notes to explain detail and a glossary of some of the terms he uses.

WALES

The first visit was made to Wales in the late 1930's, as part of a trip to the Forest of Dean but no more were made until the late 1940's. Thereafter he was a frequent visitor, and soon after his appointment at Bath University made a detailed survey of mining sites in the Welsh valleys, accompanied by Bryan Davies. It appears this was made for the National Museum of Wales.

Inevitably he concentrated on South Wales, but there are a handful of sites in mid and north Wales. Among these are records of quarrying locomotives. A valuable feature is the inclusion of numerous records of iron making and tinplate working, as well as mining.

The tinplate material is important for he covered both pack and continuous strip rolling mills, at a time when the industry was rapidly approaching extinction. A useful and detailed account of rolling mill engines is in George Watkins, *The Steam Engine in Industry*, Vol 2, 1972, pp 86-109.

Other sites included a handful of water mills, and a number associated with the docks at Newport and Cardiff. He also recorded the pumping engines at the Severn Tunnel.

FURTHER READING

John Cornwell, *Collieries of South Wales*, Vol 1, 2001, Vol 2, 2002.

Laurence Ince *The South Wales Iron Industry, 1750–1885*, 1993.

Laurence Ince. *The Neath Abbey Ironworks and the South Wales Iron Trade*. 2002

CHESHIRE

In Cheshire the sites he visited related predominantly to textile mills, though he also saw waterworks, and sites relating to the docks at Birkenhead.

SHROPSHIRE

Comparatively few sites were visited in Shropshire, but they include a number relating to Ironbridge, and also several ploughing and traction engines seen on farms.

The county order used reflects the pre-1970s arrangement under which the SER are entered on the master SER index. Thus Denbighshire entries are now in Wrexham Maelor Borough.

Beam engine, the original form as made by Boulton and Watt. This form owed its existence to the fact that all the earlier steam engines were used for pumping water, the beam forming a convenient means of attachment for the pump rods.

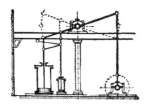

Horizontal Engine, with open frame cast iron bedplate, a type much used for all sizes of engine for general purposes. The bed-plate frame was of a U section, and was bolted down to a foundation of masonry or brickwork, the cylinder, main bearing and guides being bolted to the bed-plate.

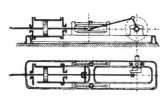

Vertical engine, a type used extensively for both large and small engines; it had the advantage of occupying little floor space. An endless number of varieties of this type was developed, and was the generally accepted type for marine screw-propeller engines.

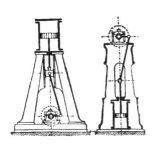

Corliss frame or Girder Engine, a type of horizontal engine. This example had a bored guide, but they were also made with flat-planed guides. In both cases the guides were formed in the main casting or girder which connects the cylinder to the main bearing. There were many varieties of this type.

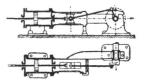

Self contained horizontal engines, with bent or slotted out cranks. This type, largely used for small power short-stroke engines had the cylinder bolted on to the end of an open bedplate, which was widened out at the other end to take both bearings of the crank shaft, so that the flywheel might be keyed on either side. The guides were usually formed in the bedplate, the boring out of the guides and facing of the end flange being done at the same setting.

Oscillating Engines, formerly much used as marine engines. Originally developed for driving paddle wheels, this type has also been used for driving screw propellers. Uncommon in land use.

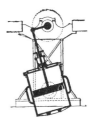

Steeple engine, formerly used for driving paddle wheels. A variety of this type had been used for small powers, and was known as the Table Engine.

Beam Engine, Woolf's Compound. Two unequal cylinders side by side, at one end of the beam. Many pumping engines were of this type.

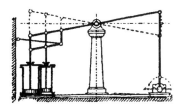

McNaught Compound Beam Engine. This system consisted of a small cylinder (high-pressure cylinder), placed at the opposite end of the beam to the larger cylinder, was introduced by McNaught for increasing the power of existing engines. The high-pressure cylinder was the one added, the original cylinder being the low-pressure cylinder. The power of the engine was thus increased by increase of boiler pressure and the addition of the new small cylinder, to which the boiler was admitted. (See glossary for more details).

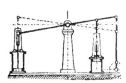

Inclined Frame Engines, used extensively for paddle steamers in several different varieties, usually compound engines.

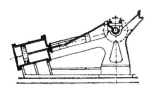

A Double-Cylinder Engine, derived from the above, with the cylinder inclined at an angle of about 45^0, was occasionally used for driving rolling mills in bar iron works.

Radial Engines. (Brotherhood type) A recent type, of which there were many varieties, in both 3 and 4 cylinder configurations. These were used for driving fans, steam launches and other applications requiring speed and compactness.

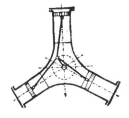

Central Valve Engines (Willans type) A modern design, single acting, compound or triple expansion configuration; a special feature was the hollow piston rod and central valve. Extensively used for driving dynamos coupled direct on to the armature shaft.

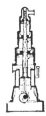

Various ways of arranging cylinders and cranks in double and three-cylinder compound and triple expansion engines

Double cylinder, with cranks at 180^0

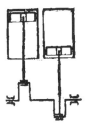

Three-cylinder engine, with cranks at 120^0

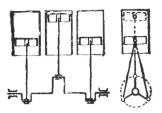

Compound Woolf engine with cranks together

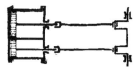

Compound Woolf engine with cranks at 180⁰

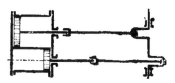

Compound Tandem engine with receiver

Compound engine with cylinders side by side with receiver cranks at 90⁰

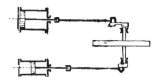

Triple expansion engine with cylinders side by side; cranks at 120⁰

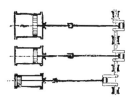

Triple expansion engine, semi-tandem; two cranks at 90⁰

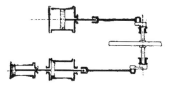

Simple slide valve

This consisted of an inverted metal box sliding on the ported face of the cylinder. It controlled the admission and exhaust of the steam to both ends of the cylinder and exhausted beneath the box valve

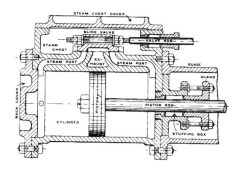

Simple piston valve

This consisted of a turned bobbin, working in a bored liner. It worked on the same principle as the slide valve.

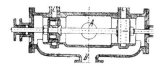

Simple valve gears

These valves were operated by simple eccentric motions of various patterns, and many allowed variable cut-off of the steam as well as reversing.

The Corliss

This was a semi-circular semi-rotating valve working in a bored liner. Separate valves were provided for steam and exhaust at each end of the cylinder, so there were four in number. A trip gear operated the valves.

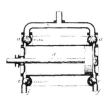

Drop valves

These were circular with taper faces, which fitted upon similar faces fitted to the cylinder. The faces were ground together to make them steam tight. The valves were lifted to admit steam and dropped by the trip gear to cut off the admission. A variety of this pattern was simple bobbins fitted with piston rings.

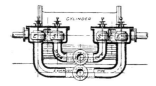

The Uniflow

This had admission valves only since the steam exhausted through a ring of ports in the centre of the cylinder barrel.

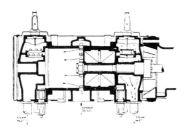

BOILERS

Cornish boilers contained a single flue

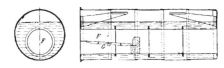

Lancashire boilers contained twin flues

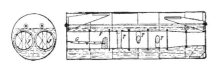

Multitibular boilers were of various types including the locomotive

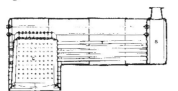

Vertical boilers were of various types. Used in very small plants

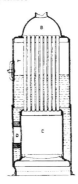

Watertube boilers were of various types.

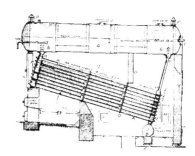

POWER TRANSMISSION

Rope drives, taking power from the engine to the floors of a mill, were usual in textile mills. In older mills power was often transmitted by a vertical shaft.

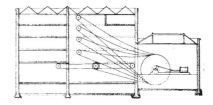

Flat belts of leather or rubberized canvas drove individual machines from a line shaft powered by the rope drive.

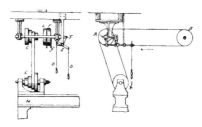

Mining

Winding engines were almost invariably made with two cylinders having cranks at 90^0, allowing good control by the engine driver. A winding engine was required to work intermittently, starting a heavy load from rest, bringing this load up with great velocity, and bringing it to rest again. This had to be done at great speed in a short time, since a great number of winds were needed daily to raise an economic quantity of coal. For this, the engine needed to be powerful and to be under precise control of the engineman at all times.

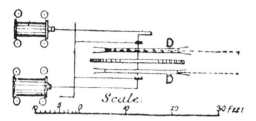

Balancing was done by fixing a rope similar to the winding rope to the bottom of each cage, the rope hanging in a loop down the pit shaft, ensuring a perpetual balance-weight equal to the winding-rope.

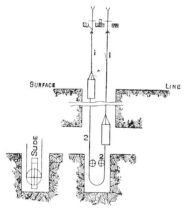

Another method of balancing was by means of the scroll or spiral drum. As the engine proceeded to wind up, the rope was wound in spiral grooves on a continually increasing diameter of drum. The other rope to the descending cage was wound off at an opposing rate so creating a counterbalance. The variation in diameter of the two sides of the drum had the effect of loading the engine proportional to the effort it needed at different stages of the wind.

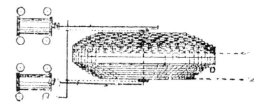

Winding was done by steam, utilising different types of pithead gear.

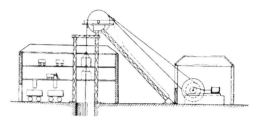

Ventilation was done by various patterns of steam driven rotary fan.

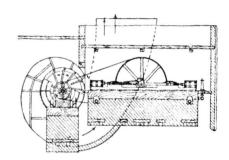

Glossary

Air pump. This removed the condensed water and air contained in the steam. It was normally driven by the engine itself.

Arbor. An axle or spindle.

Barring. This was the action of gently rotating the engine to make possible adjustments during maintenance. It was done by a lever mechanism which engaged in a series of holes cast in the face or side of the flywheel rim. A variation involved a hand or small steam engine-driven gear engaging in gear teeth cast on the inside of the flywheel rim.

Calender. A finishing machine designed to impart lustre and smoothness to woven fabrics. It comprised a series of rolls geared vertically, through which the cloth ran.

Condensers. These were airtight chambers into which the exhaust steam passed for cooling back to warm water. Cooling was by a jet of cold water which mixed with the condensate, or, in the surface type, the cold water passed through a number of small tubes to condense the steam outside them.

Count. The measure of yarns by length and weight stating how many hanks of a given length will weigh a pound: the higher the number, the finer the yarn. There were different units of length for different yarns, e.g. cotton, wool, and jute and, in the wool trade, different locations.

Dram or tram. A wheeled tub for conveying coal at the colliery.

Duff coal. Small coal unsuitable for retail sale. Used for firing boilers at collieries.

Economiser. A system of pre-heating boiler feed-water, using the heat of the waste gases in the boiler flues. First invented in 1843 by Edward Green of Wakefield, Yorks.

Edge tools. These were any kind of hand tool with a sharp cutting edge, such as a spade, hoe, sickle or scythe. A strip of toughened steel was forged as a sandwich between softer metal, and then sharpened. This was an ancient craft, some of the sites utilising water-powered tilt hammers.

Egg-ended boiler. A horizontal cylindrical boiler with hemispherical ends and no flues. At early pattern, superseded by the Cornish and Lancashire types.

Flitches. The two halves of the beam of a beam engine. Originally cast solid, beams were sometimes made in two halves and kept apart by spacers and bolts.

Glands. These were recessed bosses in the cylinder cover or valve chest of a steam engine or pump which were fitted with fibre or metal packing. They allowed the rods to work freely without leaking steam or water.

Governor. This device controlled the speed of the engine, if it was too fast or too slow, by regulating the steam supply. There were many patterns but all depended on rotating weights which adjusted the control mechanism.

Grid. The National Grid, the national electricity supply system, was begun in the 1920s. Before it became very widespread by the 1950s, many small towns and larger businesses generated their own supplies, with varying supply standards.

Hoppit or hoppet. A large basket used in mining.

Lodge. A pond located near a mill's engine-house which held the engine's condensing water. More common where the site was not previously water powered.

Manhattan engine. This was a design which coupled a horizontal and a vertical engine driving to the same crank pin. The idea surfaced around 1870 and reached its zenith in the engines driving the Manhattan (New York) power stations in the early 1900s. A number were made by various makers for use in Britain, driving textile mills, rolling mills and London Tramways power generation.

McNaughting was patented by William McNaught of Glasgow in 1845. Piston loads were thus opposed, so reducing stresses on the beam centre. The fitting of high pressure boilers and compound working gave great economy.

Mule. Cotton spinning machine, invented by Crompton, so named because it incorporated the roller-drawing principle of Arkwright's water frame and the carriage drawing of Hargreave's spinning jenny. The first successful self-acting mule was invented by Richard Roberts 1830.

Non-dead centre engines. These were vertical or horizontal engines in which two parallel cylinders were coupled to a single crank pin by a triangular connecting rod, and had the advantage of starting at almost any crank position. Twin or quadruple cylinder compound engines were common. Their heyday was 1880-1907.

Northrop loom. An automatic loom invented by 1894 by J. H. Northrop in the USA.

Overwinding gear. This was an apparatus to stop a winding engine lifting a cage beyond the pit bank and damaging itself and contents on the pit frame. Various systems were used.

Process steam. This was steam after it had left the engine and before it was condensed. It was used in the plant for other purposes such as central heating, heating dye vats, drying paper.

Rastrick Boiler. A pattern of vertical boiler which utilised the waste heat from wrought iron-making processes.

Ring spinning. A system where the spinning spindle revolves within a ring, with a small steel hoop on the flange of the ring to govern the winding-on of the thread.

Room and Power. The term means that a capitalist established a factory with a power supply (usually steam), and heating, and rented out space to small craftsmen or manufacturers. Each floor had a drive shaft taken from the engine from which individual machines, owned and worked by the tenants, were driven.

Shear. Mechanical scissors used for cropping billets of steel during the rolling process.

Sizing. The stiffening of fabrics with various pastes or starches.

Slow banking. This involved the means of controlling the winding engine carefully to allow precise location of the cage at the finish of the wind.

Tentering or stentering. This was the action of stretching cloth whilst drying to ensure all the threads were in line. Originally done by hand, latterly by machine.

SOURCES

Definitions and illustrations used have been drawn from:

Wilfred Lineham, *A text book of Mechanical Engineering*, 9ed, 1906.

Arnold Lupton, *Mining*, 3ed, 1906.

William S. Murphy, The *Textile Industries*, 8 vol, 1910.

Herman Haeder and H. H. P. Powles, *Handbook on the Steam Engine*, 4ed, 1914.

More detailed technical information about engine design may be found in:

Colin Bowden, 'The stationary steam engine: a critical bibliography', *Industrial Archaeology Review*, XV, (1992-3), pp 177-194.

George Watkins, *The Stationary Steam Engine*, 1968.

George Watkins, *The Textile Mill Engine*, 2 vol, 1970, 1971 (reprinted Landmark Publishing, 1 vol, 1999).

George Watkins, & R. A. Buchanan, *Man and the Steam Engine*, 1975, 2ed 1978.

R. A. Buchanan & George Watkins, *The Industrial Archaeology of the Stationary Steam Engine*, (1976) This is a very authoritative account of the evolution of design and construction.

George Watkins. *The Steam Engine in Industry*, 2 vol, (1978, 1978). The linking passages describing the application of steam to different industries are specially valuable.

Transactions of the Newcomen Society, especially:

Arnold Throp 'Some notes on the history of the Uniflow Steam Engine', vol 43 (1970-71) pp 19-39.

George Watkins, 'The development of the Steam Winding Engine' vol 50, (1978-79), pp 11-24.

James L. Wood, 'The introduction of the Corliss Engine into Britain', vol 52, (1980-81) pp 1-13.

R. L. Hills, 'The Uniflow engine, a reappraisal' vol 57, (1985-6) , pp 59-77.

R. W. M. Clouston, 'The development of the Babcock Boiler in Britain up to 1939', vol 58, (1986-87), pp 75-87.

James L. Wood. 'The Sulzer steam engine comes to Britain', vol 59, (1987-88), pp 129-152.

Stationary Power (The Journal of the International Steam Engine Society), especially:

William D. Sawyer, Corliss Man and engine, 2 vol, 1994, (JISSES 10), 1997, (JISSES 13).

Caernarvonshire

1) Bethesda, Penrhyn Slate Quarries   SER 652a

Type:	Vertical boilered locomotive
Photo taken:	1954
Maker and Date:	De Winton & Co., Caernarfon, 1877
Cylinder/dimensions:	No other data
Hp:	*Rpm:* *Psi:*
Service:	Quarry haulage

This is the outside frame design of quarry locomotive, i.e. with the wheels outside of the frame, but otherwise there was little difference to SER 651. The only lubrication provided for the bearings was simple drilled holes; there were no oil boxes or wick feeds for continuous oiling.

2) Bethesda, Penrhyn Slate Quarries   SER 652b

Type:	Water Balance Hoists
Photo taken:	1954
Maker and Date:	Maker unknown – De Winton ?
Cylinder/dimensions:	
Hp:	*Rpm.* *Psi:*
Service:	Slate hoists. Raised 2 tons 75 yds high in shafts

These worked by filling a water tank suspended below the cage. When the weight of water overcame that of the dram of slate in the cage at the bottom, the cage was raised under the control of the brake. The hoisting ropes were usually flat 6in x $^1/_4$ in thick and the tank under the cage about 6ft by 9ft by 3ft deep. The water discharged and flowed away by gravity, the deepest part being hundreds of feet above sea level. These hoists, the last of many used in Wales, were used until the quarries closed as demand for slates fell off.

3) Llanberis, Dinorwic Quarry   SER 687

Type:	High breast water wheel rim drive
Photo taken:	1954
Maker and Date:	De Winton & Co., Caernarfon, 1870
Cylinder/dimensions:	50ft 0in diameter by 5ft 0in wide
Hp:	*Rpm.* *Psi:*
Service:	Slate factory drive

A very fine suspension type wheel, this drove the workshops for over fifty years until replaced by a water turbine. The arms were held into the boss by cotters, and there was very little distortion of the rim.

3

4) Llanberis, Dinorwic Quarry   SER 687a

Type:	Early main line locomotive
Photo taken:	1954
Maker and Date:	Northfleet Ironworks, Kent, c. 1840s
Cylinder/dimensions:	
Hp:	*Rpm:* *Psi:*
Service:	Preserved.

The inclined cylinders and long wheelbase were early design features, as were the Salter's balance safety valves. The whole was unaltered. *Fire Queen* as she was called was last used in 1886.

5) Llanberis, Dinorwic Quarry   SER 687c

Type:	Circular firebox 4 coupled locomotive *Sybil*
Photo taken:	1954
Maker and Date:	W. G. Bagnall Ltd., Stafford, No 1760
Cylinder/dimensions:	Slide valves
Hp:	*Rpm:* *Psi:*
Service:	Slate quarry transport

Circular fireboxes allowed extra water carrying capacity under the frame, and the four coupled drive made them easy on sharp curves, and indifferent tracks. The Baguley Price valve gear also suffered less from the violent motion on the tracks. They were thus good quarry locomotives, but must have suffered from the small volume of the firebox. *Sybil* was in steam at the quarry in 1953.

6) Llanberis, Snowdon Mountain Railway   SER 655 (2)

Type:	Rack & adhesion Locomotive No 2, *Enid*
Photo taken:	1954
Maker and Date:	Swiss Locomotive Works, Winterthur, Works No. 924, 1895
Cylinder/dimensions:	
Hp:	*Rpm:* *Psi:*
Service:	Passenger transport. Locomotive No 2

Enid was of the early design, with slide valves, using saturated steam, and with grasshopper beam motion to transfer the effect back to the wheels. There were three of each type in regular service in 1960.

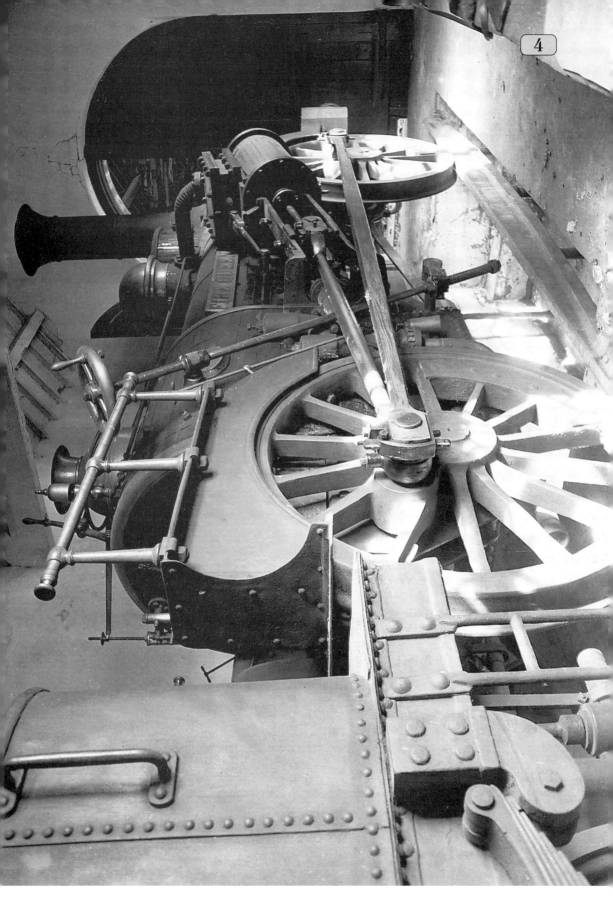

7) *Llanberis, Snowdon Mountain Railway* SER 655 (8)

Type:	Rack & adhesion Locomotive No 8, *Eryri*
Photo taken:	1954
Maker and Date:	Swiss Locomotive Works, Winterthur, c. 1923
Cylinder/dimensions:	
Hp:	*Rpm:* *Psi:*
Service:	Passenger transport. Locomotive No. 8

The locomotives differed in the coupling rod system, and valves. *Eryri* was of the later design with equal beam motion to transfer the effect back to the wheels, and these later ones also had piston valves and superheaters. The boilers of all were inclined to suit the gradient.

8) *Nantlle, Dorothea Quarry* SER 653

Type:	Cornish beam
Photo taken:	1954
Maker and Date:	Holman Bros., Camborne, 1904.
Cylinder/dimensions:	68in x 10ft 0in – 9ft 0in for pump
Hp: ?	*Spm:* $6^{1}/_{2}$ *Psi:* 40
Service:	Slate quarry pump. Raised 110 gallons per stroke from 330ft deep

This was replaced by a submersible electrically driven pump in the 1950s, when coal was becoming too costly for quarry useage. It was a typical late Cornish engine with the corrugated casing for the lagging which Harveys used latterly. This engine was designed by N. Trestrail, and had given good service. The quarry closed in 1972, and the Cornish engine left in situ.

9) *Nantlle, Dorothea Quarry* SER 653a

Type:	Horizontal non-condensing single cylinder
Photo taken:	1954
Maker and Date:	De Winton, Caernarfon, 1869
Cylinder/dimensions:	12in x 2ft 0in – Slide valve
Hp:	*Rpm:* *Psi:*
Service:	Moving and raising slate about the quarry hole

A typical sound design which was arranged so that the drive could readily be taken from either side. There were pads for the main bearings cast on either side of the bedplate, and the guides and cylinder could be used either side. The jaw end of the connecting rod and split crosshead were desirable features for ease of maintenance and link motion reverse gear was fitted. It remained as built, even retaining the old style flywheel with wrought iron arms cast into the hub and rim, which was the brake track. These steam telphers were replaced by electrically driven units later.

10) Nantlle, Dorothea Quarry   SER 653b

Type:	Overtype double cylinder non-condensing
Photo taken:	1954
Maker and Date:	Ashby, Jeffery & Luke, Stamford, No 231, c. 1870s
Cylinder/dimensions:	10in x 1ft 6in – Slide valves
Hp:	*Rpm:* *Psi:*
Service:	Telpher hoisting and transfer drive

This was a rare make in which the boiler was completely derelict, and. barely able to stand the working strains of the engine, which was latterly steamed from a Lancashire boiler which also steamed another engine. The Ashby had been used to raise the slate in the quarry and. transfer it by the telpher carriages to the railway system but the steam plant had all gone from the quarry when it closed in 1971 except for the Holman Cornish beam pump which was superseded by a submersible electric unit in the 1950s. The Cornish engine is preserved but all else has gone.

11) Nantlle, Pen-y-Bryn Old Mill   SER 1413

Type:	Vertical single cylinder condensing
Photo taken:	1970
Maker and Date:	Mather (Liverpool) ?, 1850s?
Cylinder/dimensions:	18in x 3ft 0in – Slide valve
Hp: 25	*Rpm:* 60 *Psi:* ?
Service:	Plant drive by 9in belt off 5ft 0in pulley. Flywheel 11ft 0in diameter

The little mill was in a very remote spot above the large Dorothea quarry, and very little was known of its history. Nothing remained in 1970 except the engine, with a long building and a chimney 54 feet high all made of waste slate slabs; the boiler setting was outside, but the whole, long derelict, was too overgrown to check adequately. The makers plate *Mather* was stolen, they may have been Mather Dixon of Liverpool who certainly made an engine for Liverpool Waterworks in the 1830s. Two fine fluted columns supported the crankshaft bearing, and the cylinder was partly below the floor with the condensers beneath it. Despite the evident vandalism to remove all non-ferrous parts, the engine was removed under difficult weather conditions by the Industrial Steam Preservation Group, to the Dinorwic Quarry museum.

12) Nantlle, Pen-yr-Orsedd Slate Quarry   SER 654

Type:	Vertical boiler locomotive
Photo taken:	1954
Maker and Date:	De Winton, Caernarvon, 1897
Cylinder/dimensions:	6in x 8in – Slide valves
Hp:	*Rpm:* *Psi:*
Service:	Quarry transport. 24in gauge

A late example of the type, propably not many were made after this date. It differs very little from the others in Caernarvonshire, and was believed to have been broken up about 1954.

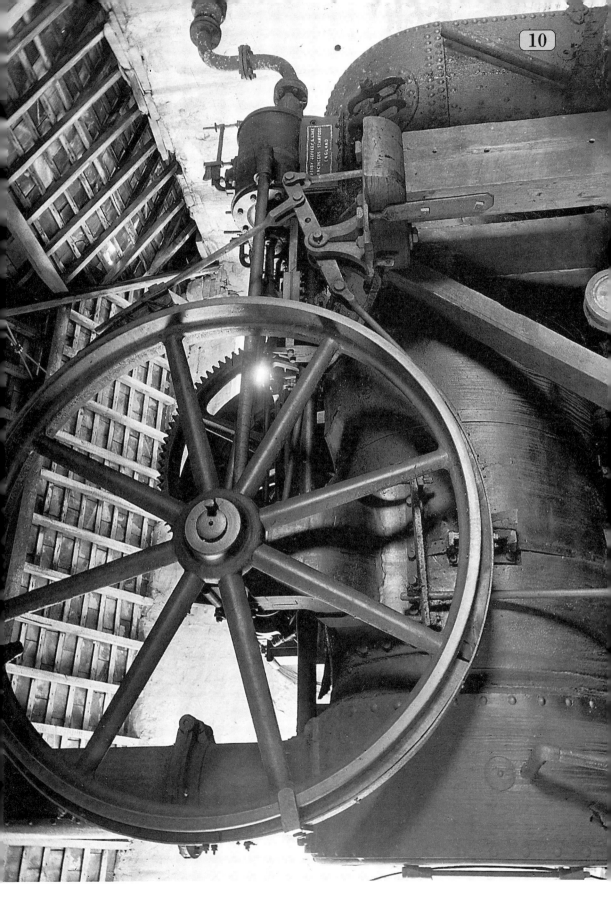

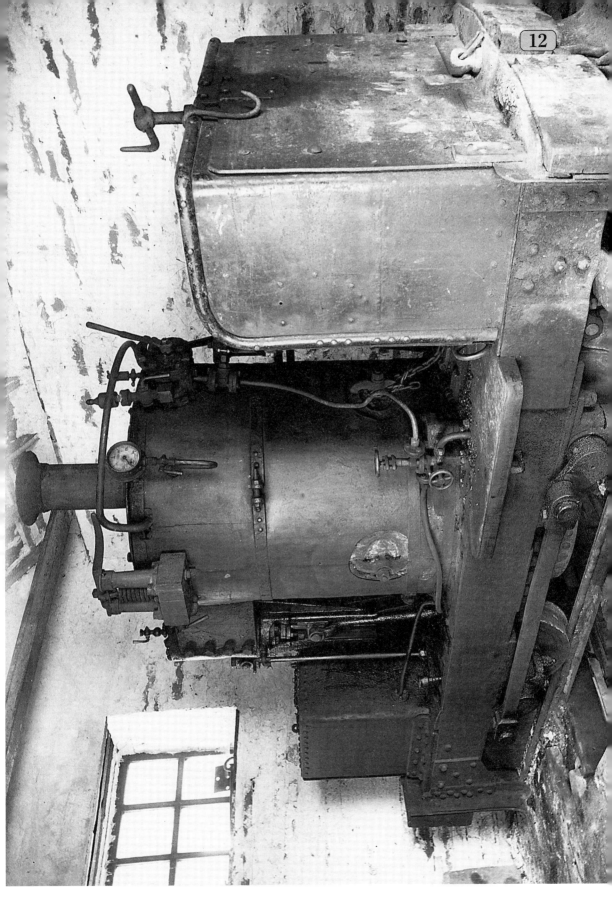

13) Penmaenmawr, Penmaenmawr Granite Quarry Co.,   SER 651

Type:	Vertical boiler locomotive
Photo taken:	1954
Maker and Date:	De Winton & Co., Caernarfon, 1893
Cylinder/dimensions:	6in x 10in – Slide valves

This was the standard De Winton locomotive for the quarries, the main variation was that some were of the inside and others the outside type. This one originally called *Wadkin* was the inside frame design. The boilers were vertical fire tube type, and this had 92 tubes.

Carmarthenshire

14) Abergwili, nr Carmarthen, Messrs Abels, Woollen Mill, Cwmgwili
SER 964

Type:	Overshot water wheel drive by gearing to dynamo		
Photo taken:	1959		
Maker & Date:	Carmarthen Foundry Co., Date unknown		
Cylinders:	12ft 0in diameter x 4ft 0in		
Hp:	*Rpm:*	*Psi:*	

The mill had long been water-powered, but latterly electrical driving was installed and the water power assisted this from a generator. The wheel was a lightly built suspension type with flat arms, and there was also another one which had been removed, as the water supply fell off. It was, however, used in the 1950's to assist the Grid current used. Very simply made by a local concern it gave very little trouble in some 60-70 years working. The main product was Welsh flannelling and the whole was a typical country economy unit, which however sent flannel over a wide area.

15) Kidwelly, Kidwelly Tinplate Co.,   SER 943

Type:	Inverted vertical tandem compound		
Photo taken:	1958		
Maker & Date:	Edwin Foden, Sandbach, 1870s		
Cylinders:	24in and 48in x 4ft 0in – Piston valves		
Hp: Approx 400	*Rpm:* 30	*Psi:* 120	
Service:	Hot rolls drive 24ft flywheels, direct to mills. All dimensions are approximate – no records		

This was a celebrated early tinplate-making site, and the original works were water driven, and a short distance away. The history was very confused, but the engines were probably installed as 48in single cylinders using steam at 50-60 psi in the early 1870s and made tandem compound in 1892 (the date of the water tube boilers) by the addition, either by Price of Llanelly, or Neville's of Neath, of 24in bore piston valve cylinders on the top of the original ones. They would then drive three instead of the original two mills each. They worked thus until 1941, when tinplate making finally ceased on the site. It is possible that one engine drove the cold rolls at one time, but new cold rolls driven by a Cole, Marchent & Morley drop piston valve tandem engine were installed in 1921, with a higher pressure Lancashire boiler. It was said that at one time nearly 900 hands worked at the plant, some coming from Burry Port. These were the last remaining hot rolling mills of the pack mill hand tinplate making trade, once a leading industry of South Wales.

16) Llanelli, Dafen Co., Dafen   SER 850

Type:	Superposed compound horizontal condensing
Photo taken:	1957
Maker & Date:	Galloways Ltd., 1890s
Cylinders:	13in and 22in x 2ft 9in
Hp: 240	*Rpm:* 95 *Psi:* 160
Service:	Cold rolling mill drive

Following upon the success of the first ones they supplied for the cold rolling or finishing stages of tinplate sheet making, Galloways supplied many of these in South Wales. Almost all of these remained as built, but when Musgraves supplied new hot rolling mill engines to Dafen which with higher steam pressure were more economical, they also altered the Galloway superposed engines by fitting Musgrave Corliss valve high pressure cylinders to each (Dafen was one of the very few works which had two cold roll engines). This work was done about 1911, and the engines ran thus until they were closed at the end of the pack mill trade, when strip replaced the individual sheet pack mill process, in the late 1950's.

17) Llanelli, Gorse Galvanising Co., Dafen   SER 941

Type:	Horizontal cross compound
Photo taken:	1958
Maker & Date:	Hick, Hargreaves & Co., Bolton, 1912
Cylinders:	33in and 64in x 6ft 0in – Corliss valves
Hp: 1190	*Rpm:* 30 *Psi:* 150
Service:	Direct drive to hot rolling mills

This was typical of the latest development in tinplate rolling, in which a massive engine with double cranks on each side, drove the mills directly by wobbler couplings from the crankshaft. Six mills were usually driven off one engine this way, whereas four was the most previously. These later engines were heavily built, and reliable, since there was no transmission gearing of any sort. The flywheel was very heavy, the rim in this case being 30in deep by 18in wide, and these were often supplied by local foundries. Despite the heavy shock loads, the engines were massive enough to give reliable service, and repairs, other than routine wear and tear, were rare. The flywheel in this case was in 10 sections and so probably made by Hick, Hargreaves with the engine. All was scrapped with the end of the hand mills.

18) Llanelli, Llanelli Sheet Mill Co.,   SER 934

Type:	Uniflow single cylinder
Photo taken:	1958
Maker & Date:	Galloways Ltd., Manchester, 1923
Cylinders:	40in x 4ft 0in ?
Hp: 1800	*Rpm:* 140 *Psi:* 170
Service:	Hot sheet rolling. Mill drive by 40 ropes

This was the latest development in sheet mill driving, having the Pilling oil valve gear, and with the Galloways flexible rear supporting columns, which gave the cylinder complete freedom from expansion stresses due to the foundation, i.e. it was only tied to the engine bed at the front, and then held by the swinging stays at the back. It was not bolted down to the foundation in any way. It was heavily loaded, and ran continuously throughout the week for many years, driving 6 sheet mills each with the usual two stands of rolls per mill. The tail piston rod guide was fitted when the engine was built, and throughout, the engine was Lancashire engineering of high order. It well paid its way until, with the development of the strip sheet mills, the plant was closed, in the 1960s.

19) Llanelli, South Wales Steel Works   SER 947

Type:	Twin cylinder horizontal non condensing
Photo taken:	1958
Maker & Date:	Daniel Adamson & Co., Dukinfield, 1890s
Cylinders:	40in x 4ft 6in – Piston valves
Hp: 4000	*Rpm:* max 90-100 *Psi:* 140
Service:	Cogging mill for steel ingots to sheet bars

The works had been greatly extended, and this engine, originally fitted with slide valves, was converted to piston valves when the pressure was increased as the other engine (a Lamberton three cylinder) was installed about 1910. It was an unusual layout in that the roughing and finishing mills were side by side, and, originally driven by the Adamson, were later separately driven by this, and a Lamberton three cylinder installed for the finishing side. When the Lamberton engine was extensively overhauled in 1952, the Adamson drove both mills for a period, but later settlement of one mill made this impossible. All of the plant was scrapped quite late, about 1962-3. It was very well kept.

20) Llangennech, Morlais Colliery   SER 1317a

Type:	Horizontal cross compound
Photo taken:	1967
Maker & Date:	Andrew Barclay Sons & Co., Kilmarnock, c. 1907
Cylinders:	15in and 24in x 2ft 6in – Slide valves
Hp: ?	*Rpm:* 120 *Psi:* 90
Service:	Coal winding from the Swansea 5ft. Seam 105yds deep, on 1 in 6 incline. 600yds long

Fitted with bored trunk guides, disc cranks and Stephenson's link motion, this was hauling up the drift from the pit, and was very powerful, being geared down over 3 to 1 to the rope drum shaft. It probably hauled up only, lowering the drams by gravity. The main coal drawing was done later by the vertical shaft winder, SER 1317b, but the drift engine was certainly well used for materials, and was economical since it was compound.

21) Llangennech, Morlais Colliery   SER 1317b

Type:	Horizontal double cylinder
Photo taken:	1967
Maker & Date:	Andrew Barclay Sons & Co., Kilmarnock, 1907
Cylinders:	20in x 2ft 0in – Corliss valves
Hp: ?	*Rpm:* 60 *Psi:* 90
Service:	Winder for vertical shaft. Rope drum 8ft diameter

Although dash pots were fitted for releasing trip gear, for the Corliss valves, no trips were fitted and the valves were always connected directly to the circular wrist plates, as can be seen in the farther cylinder. It was Barclay's later design in all details, neat and strong, and with circular section eccentric rods, trunk guides and plain Stephenson's link motion reversing gear. The whole colliery was very well kept and the engines were neatly painted, and cleaned. It was very fast, making the 105 yards wind in 22 seconds, completing the winding cycle in 30 seconds. Steam was cut-off usually in $4^{1}/_{2}$ out of the total of $12^{3}/_{4}$ revolutions of the full wind. The engine was purchased new by Thos. Williams in 1907, which may date the change from originally the incline working to vertical shaft winding. There was a Cornish beam engine house probably with rods following the incline.

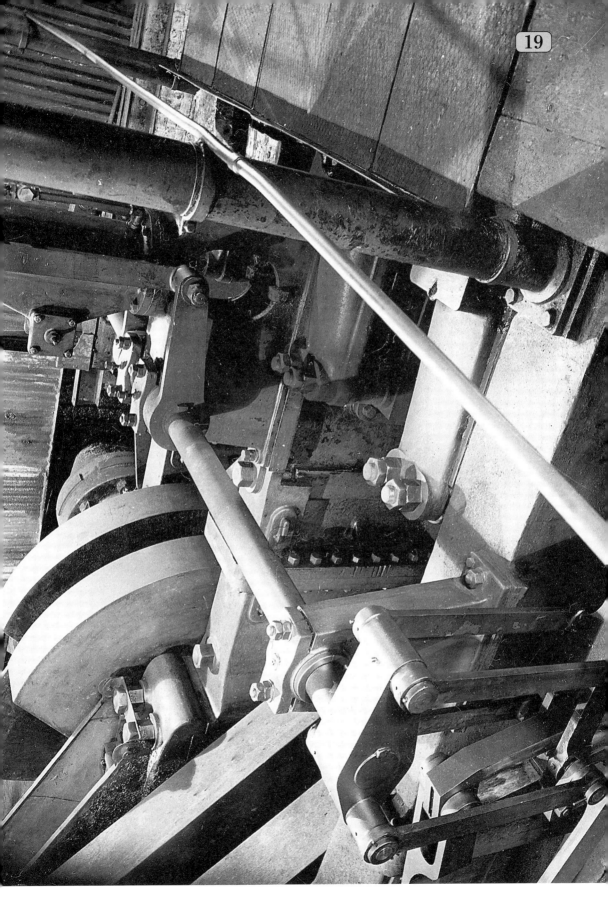

Denbighshire

22) Brymbo, Brymbo Iron & Steel Works   SER 1118

Type:	Inverted vertical twin cylinder non-condensing
Photo taken:	1963
Maker and Date:	Davy Bros, Sheffield, c. 1875
Cylinder/dimensions:	38in x 4ft 6in – Circular grid valves
Hp: 400	*Rpm:* 36 *Psi:* 75
Service:	Blast furnace blowers. Air cylinders on top 72in x 4ft 6in

This was remarkable in that there was no standby engine, although it was on a service where continuous operation was essential as a blast failure and cold furnace was a serious risk. However it was kept working by the engineers for over 70 years. It was always non-condensing and quite economical. The steam valves were unique, being plain circular grid plugs working across the cylinder, with separate valves for the inlet, and exhaust, at each end. They were not fitted with packing rings of any sort, just plain circular discs about $\frac{1}{2}$in wide, with $\frac{1}{2}$in wide spaces, and very short travel, with a cam motion to give rapid cut–off movement. It was an outstanding example of an unusual design which proved sound in all ways, and certainly was unique. A turbine blower was installed about 1963-4 but all was scrapped when iron making was discontinued in 1970. It was worthy of preservation, as certainly a rare design of steam valves.

23) Llay, nr. Wrexham, Llay Main Colliery   SER 1327a

Type:	Horizontal double cylinder
Photo taken:	1968
Maker and Date:	Markham & Co., Chesterfield, c. 1920s?
Cylinder/dimensions:	About 30in x 7ft 0in – Drop valves
Hp: ?	*Rpm:* 45 *Psi:* 150
Service:	Coal winding. Shaft 1,000 yds deep. Rope drum 16 to 28ft. diameter

This was Markham's latest design, with drop inlet and Corliss exhaust valves, trunk frame, and bi-cylindro-conical rope drum. The colliery was very efficiently arranged with a full low pressure steam utilisation system, with mixed pressure turbines. In 1960, a Martin stoker with Daniel Adamson boiler for 350 p.s.i. were added to assist the power system. There were two alternators and two air compressors, all mixed pressure turbine driven (see SER 1327b). In all there had been 11 Lancashire boilers, and 3 water tube, and latterly the D. Adamson boilers. The pit was, however, closed in 1968, and all was scrapped.

24) Llay, nr. Wrexham, Llay Main Colliery   SER 1327b

Type:	Mixed pressure steam turbines
Photo taken:	1968
Maker and Date:	British Thompson Houston – General Electric Co. – Belliss and another make
Service:	Power station. Electricity and compressed air supply

The power system was very complete, with some 7,000 h.p. capacity, for air compressing and electricity generation. All was contained within one power house, which also contained the Browett and Lindley compound high speed engine driving the ventilating fan (a late Waddle high speed open type). The nearest unit is the G.E.C. turbo compressor, followed by two turbo alternators, and at the left distant corner was the Browett fan engine with the rotor in the fan drift outside. The entire colliery was a credit to all concerned and it is tragic that it was closed in 1968.

25) Rossett, nr. Wrexham, The Watermills   SER 471

Type:	Three undershot waterwheels
Photo taken:	1952
Maker and Date:	Unknown
Cylinder/dimensions:	Two: 16ft 0in diameter and one: 13ft 6in. Water fall about 4ft 0in at each mill
Service:	Driving corn mills

There are two mill sites, one dating from the 16th century (sic), driven by a single large wheel, the tail water from which then passed under the road to form a pond to feed the other two wheels at the lower mill (seen in the print). The machinery drives were the usual vertical shaft and spur wheels for the stones with two pairs of stones to each waterwheel. The lower mill also contained ancillary machinery, flour sifters, corn kibblers for cattle feed, elevator, etc. An unusual feature was that the sun or large spur wheel at the upper mill was of wood with apparently metal teeth.

  Publisher's note: the upper mill is now understood to date from about 1474, the datestone on the front elevation refers to the extension of 1661. R. Lowe, *Reflections of a Bygone Age*, Allington & Burton, Rossett.

26) Ruabon, Dennis Tile Works   SER 1442

Type:	Horizontal double cylinder non-condensing	
Photo taken:	1972	
Maker and Date:	Unknown	
Cylinder/dimensions:	9in x 1ft 6in – Slide valves	
Hp:	*Rpm:* 100	*Psi:* 75
Service:	Clay haulage from pits	

One of the last of several tile and brick plants in the area, this and the Ruabon works were due to be re-sited in 1974-5. There was also a similar engine but single cylinder, driving a part of the brick presses here, most of the plant being electrically driven. The haulage engine drove through spur reduction and bevel gearing to a vertical shaft on which was mounted a horizontal clip drum around which endless hauling cable passed down into the pit, and around a tension pulley at the bottom, and returning up the incline to the clip drum. The drams of clay were hauled by knots in the cable which caught in "Y"-shaped forks on the tops of the drams, the cable being above the drams. The knots were engaged by pushing the dram under the cable until a knot caught in the fork, and hauled the dram some 600 feet up the incline to the top of the works, which allowed the clay to feed to the crushing and tempering sections by gravity. This engine was remote controlled from the landing platform above, and the whole very simple, hauling the clay over half a mile from the workings.

27) Ruabon, Ruabon Brick & Terra Cotta Co.   SER 1441

Type:	Horizontal single cylinder – non-condensing	
Photo taken:	1972	
Maker and Date:	Maker unknown, c. 1875?	
Cylinder/dimensions:	21in x 4ft 6in – Cornish valves	
Hp: 150	*Rpm:* 80	*Psi:* 100
Service:	Derelict, once drove entire plant	

This was probably made locally, and was really one half of a winding engine, adapted for mill driving. It drove all of the plant until, following a major overhaul in 1965, it was replaced by electrical drives in 1966. It was very plain, but heavily made, with the drop valves placed at each corner of the cylinder and provided with slip eccentric reversing gear. A governor had been added, and the main driving shaft was some 400 ft long, driving the

brick presses and tempering rolls, and at the far end was the haulage clip drum to bring the clay up from the pit. The exhaust was used under the drying kiln. An attempt made in 1935 to use a 200 h.p. motor instead of the engine failed, and the engine ran on for 30 years, when electrification was finally adopted through many motors, and the engine was stopped, although some steam was still used in the processes.

Flintshire

28) Shotton, John Summers & Co., Shotton Steel Works   SER 688

Type:	Horizontal three cylinder non-condensing. Reversing
Photo taken:	1954
Maker and Date:	Scott & Hodgson, 1917
Cylinder/dimensions:	40in x 4ft 6in – Piston valves
Hp: 12,000 peak.	*Rpm:* Up to 140 *Psi:* 160
Service:	Billet Mill

Two of these were supplied to Shotton in 1917, together with two very powerful sheet mill engines. Only this one remained in 1953, which was integrated into the works for billet rolling. It was rebuilt twice with a higher gear ratio each time, to handle heavier billets. The works steam system was re-arranged with high pressure boilers and turbines (450 psi) which exhausted into the works steam mains at 160 psi. The billet mill engine ran from this and exhausted into the works low pressure steam services. The engine and mill were removed to Park Gate Steel Works in 1956, and replaced at Shotton by a 7,000 hp motor and slabbing mill.

Glamorganshire

29) Abercynon, Abercynon Colliery   SER 682

Type:	Horizontal twin cylinder non-condensing
Photo taken:	1954
Maker and Date:	John Fowler & Co., Leeds, No 6209. 1891
Cylinder/dimensions:	42in x 7ft 0in – Drop valves
Service:	Coal winding. Depth 2,220ft

Although the engine was generally unchanged, this had new cylinders by Daglish, with Melling's trip gear fitted later, possibly to use higher steam pressure. The use of twin slide bars for the tail rods was unusual, although Fowlers did this at times. It was named *Fair Rosamund*. New cranks and a crankshaft were fitted by Markhams in 1956, but the colliery was closed under later re-organisation schemes.

30) Bargoed, Bargoed Colliery   SER 681

Type:	Combined vertical and horizontal
Photo taken:	1954
Maker and Date:	Thornewill & Warham, No. 834, 1900
Cylinder/dimensions:	32in and 50in x 6ft 0in – Corliss valves – each side
Service:	Coal winding. Shaft 1,890ft deep. Drum 16ft to 24ft 0in

This was an unusual design, for high power and good balance. The high pressure cylinders were horizontal, with the vertical low pressures connected to the same crank pins. This latterly had a diabolo drum with the conical part on the inner or central section. The pits were involved in the general re-organising of the trade on Nationalisation, when much good plant was scrapped.

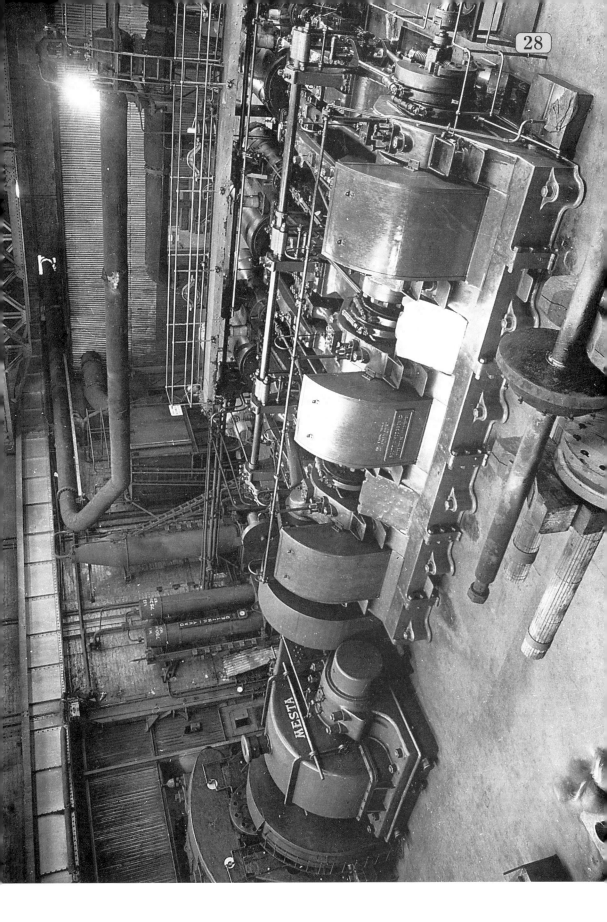

31) Blaencwm, Glenrhondda Colliery (The Old Shaft)   SER 1309

Type:	Horizontal double cylinder
Photo taken:	1967
Maker and Date:	Maker and date unknown
Cylinder/dimensions:	c. 20in x 4ft 0in – Slide valves
Hp: Not running	*Rpm:* *Psi:*
Service:	Was coal winding. Shaft c. 170yds deep. 1½ tons coal per wind

This was first installed at another pit, possibly Cilely?, and was removed to a site near Fernhill, and finally came to the Old Shaft as a second shaft winder. There was no name plate, or anything in the design to suggest a maker, but again it was a plain substantial unit which gave little trouble. The design suggested the 1880s as a date, and little had been altered in the removals. An electrical winding engine was installed at the pit in 1954, and with less demand for steam, the boilers were scrapped and the engine put on to compressed (or blast) air.

32) Briton Ferry, Briton Ferry Ironworks   SER 955

Type:	Two Inverted vertical single cylinder non-condensing
Photo taken:	1958
Maker and Date:	Richardson, Westgarth, Hartlepool, 1909, No 343
Cylinder/dimensions:	42in x 45ft 0in – Corliss valves
Hp: Approx. 450	*Rpm:* 25 *Psi:* 120
Service:	Blast furnace blower. Air cylinders 72in x 5ft 0in

linder nearest with the air cylinder on the other side of the flywheel, driven by its own crank on the same shaft. The engines were run non-condensing, this one having been purchased new to replace a beam engine and the other came from Blaina Ironworks when they closed in about 1918. The quarter crank design, as it was called, was a purely American design and developed by the Southwark Foundry Co. of Philadelphia, with cam operated grid valves on the air cylinders. All of the plant was scrapped when the works was closed about 1960, as the demand for the haematite pig iron they made ceased, probably with the pack mill tinplate business.

33) Cardiff, Cardiff Docks Hydraulic Pumping Station   SER 819

Type:	One horizontal – six inverted vertical
Photo taken:	1956
Maker and Date:	Horizontal = W.G. Armstrong, Newcastle
	Verticals = Hydraulic Engineering Co., Chester
Service:	Hydraulic Power Supply. Water to 800 psi

Cardiff Docks hydraulic plant was in one station, with six units (Docks No. 677 to 682). The horizontal was a twin tandem with cylinders about 22in and 36in x 3ft 0in stroke, and the others 18in – 26in and 40in x 2ft 6in – all with slide valves. The horizontal pumps were off the piston tail rods and the verticals above the crankshaft, directly off the piston rods. It was probably the largest hydraulic power plant in a British dock, but, largely disused with the fall in the coal shipping trade, the main use latterly was for lock gate and capstan service, and this was met by small electric sets as long as the docks were in use. The steam plant probably dated from the early 1890s, but there were variations in the individual units and the verticals may have been of differing dates.

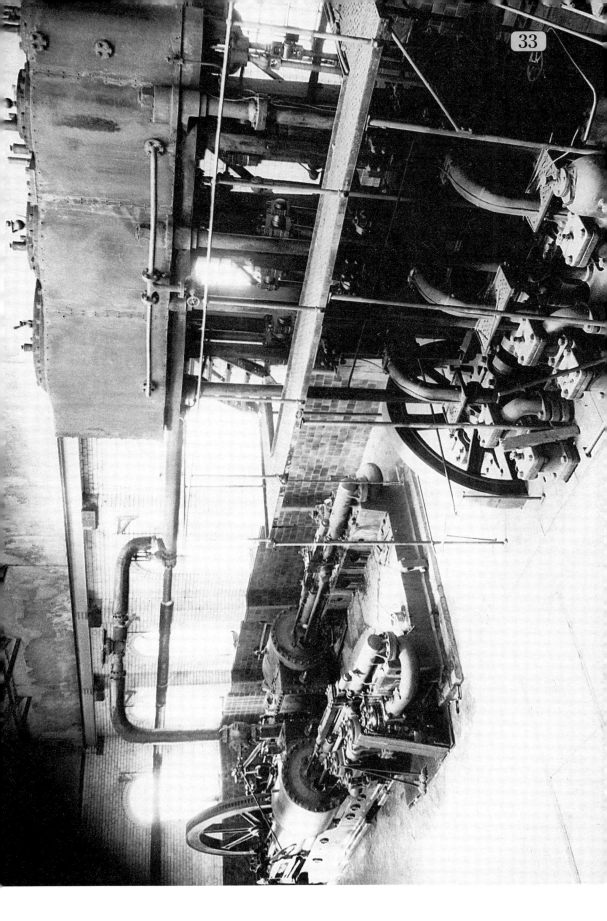

34) Cardiff, Canal Pump, Melingriffith, Whitchurch   SER 820

Type:	Undershot waterwheel
Photo taken:	1956
Maker and Date:	Maker unknown – 1810?
Cylinder/dimensions:	No dimensions available
Service:	Pumped water from Melingriffith Tinplate Works feeder to maintain Glamorgan Canal level

This is certainly the oldest water driven pumping unit remaining, with two single acting bucket pumps driven from the timber overhead beams, which are supported upon an "A" frame, also entirely of timber. The pumps were driven by cast iron arch heads from the beam ends, and the crank was unusual in that it consisted of a disc casting, with a pin for one crank, and this pin was extended to operate the other pump beam. The connecting rods were also of cast iron, as was largely the water wheel itself. Nothing was known of its capacity, but it remained in use until 1940. There is a fine model of it in the National Museum of Wales.

35) Cardiff, Melingriffith Tinplate Works, Whitchurch   SER 810

Type:	Two inverted vertical single crank tandems
Photo taken:	1956
Maker and Date:	Summers & Scott, Gloucester, 1906
Cylinder/dimensions:	13in and 26in x 3ft 0in – Slide valves
Hp: 150 max each?	*Rpm:* 80 *Psi:* 140
Service:	Tinplate making. Cold rolls for finishing plates

Melingriffith was an extensive plant with at least 8 water wheel driven mills in the mid-19th century. These were replaced by single cylinder steam engines for the hot and cold roll drives in the latter part of the century, which were compounded by Scott and Hodgson, adding tandem high pressure cylinders about 1906. Then, with new boilers and increased capacity, more cold roll power was needed and these two engines were installed. Later a 500 hp water turbine drove one line of hot mills, with a 500 hp motor as standby for dry weather. All was scrapped when the mills closed in 1958. *Publishers note:* The cards for SER 810a, 810b, 810c appear to be missing from the collection.

36) Cardiff, National Museum of Wales   SER 683

Type:	Water balance coal hoist and a beam engine
Photo taken:	1954
Service:	Open air exhibits

The water balance was used for many years at the Brynpwllog Old Shaft, nr Rhymney for coal hoisting. It consisted of a cage with a water tank beneath it, on each side of the shaft, which were connected together by a chain passing over the top pulley, which also contained the braking device for accurate landing of the cages. The operating method was to fill the tank beneath the cage at the top, until the weight of the water began to move the lower cage containing a tub of coal, the brake being used to control the speed. The water was released when the tub of coal was placed in the lower cage, and the cycle was thus completed by again filling the top tank as the lower one was emptied, the water usually passing to an adit. The beam engine was used at Lightmoor Colliery for nearly a century, to hoist the pit waste up to the tip. It was probably made by the Soudley Foundry, also in the Forest of Dean. Each were simple units readily made by local workmen and facilities, which had very long working lives with little repair, and well worth preserving.

37) Clydach, John Player & Sons, Tinplate Works   SER 963

Type:	Single cylinder uniflow
Photo taken:	1959
Maker and Date:	Hick, Hargreaves & Co., Bolton, 1914?
Cylinder/dimensions:	24in x 3ft 0in – Drop valves
Hp: Approx 250	*Rpm:* 100 *Psi:* 160
Service:	Cold roll drive

This was purchased secondhand and installed about 1922-31 and was designed for 150 rpm, but here was connected directly to the cold rolling mill shaft, and so ran slowly. Most cold roll engines were also arranged in tandem i.e. two or three sets following so that the sheets passed through each stand, whereas here they only passed through one stand. It was also unusual in that there was a piston valve to relieve the compression (the Tabourin system) which can be seen driven by eccentric from the side layshaft, near to the governor. The hot rolls were driven by a large Hick, Hargreaves Corliss valve tandem, with two mills on either side. There were three Galloway boilers. Cold rolling was continued with sheet from the Glynhir works, after hot rolling ceased about 1954, but everything was scrapped about 1960.

38) Clydach Vale, Cambrian Colliery (No 3 pit)   SER 1311

Type:	Horizontal double cylinder
Photo taken:	1967
Maker and Date:	Thornewill & Warham, 1900?
Cylinder/dimensions:	36in x 6ft 0in – Cornish valves
Service:	Was coal winding. Shaft 540yds. deep

Coal winning had been abandoned here, the engine latterly serving an escape shaft. There were certainly many features reminiscent of Thorneweill's practice, although the valve gear on the outer side was not their usual design. The station air compressor was Belliss and Morcom No. 3479 – with an 1,125 hp motor. The Cambrian group of pits was celebrated for the high quality coal in earlier days, but winning had ceased by the late 1960s; the engine was, however, test run regularly, and reasonably well kept, but the colliery closed in 1966.

39) Crynant, Cefn Coed Colliery   SER 1302

Type:	Horizontal double cylinder
Photo taken:	1967
Maker and Date:	Maker unknown. Early 1900s
Cylinder/dimensions:	9in x 1ft 0in – Slide valve
Service:	Winding waste to colliery spoil bank

This was a typical late design haulage for pit waste, where a powerful engine was needed to haul the waste up the high waste heaps. This engine was used to haul by a single rope, using the double reduction gearing to give power for the haul up the tip and returning the tubes down the track at high speed through the higher speed available through the dog clutch and the gears seen at the left. The confined sites in the valleys posed great problems as the amounts of waste increased with machine mining in later years. In some cases, new tips had to be made on top of the original ones, giving very severe gradients, and in at least one case, a second haulage engine with its own boiler was placed on the top of the old tip, to haul up to the top of the new one. To do this from one lower engine demanded very great power and high gear reductions. This engine probably had a haul of over 1,000 yards, with 8 or 10 tubs of dirt totalling 5-6 tons in all.

37

39

40) Crynant, Cefn Coed Colliery   SER 1316

Type:	Horizontal double cylinder
Photo taken:	1967
Maker and Date:	Worsley Mesnes Ltd., Wigan, 1927
Cylinder/dimensions:	32ins x 5ft. – Drop inlet and Corliss exhaust valves
Hp: Approx 800	*Rpm:* 60 *Psi:* 180
Service:	Wound coal from 2,100 ft deep

This was new to the colliery and fitted to the downcast shaft when sunk in 1927. It wound about 3 tons of coal in two tubs in an 80 second cycle, i.e. about 65 seconds to wind and 15 to change the tubs. The valves were driven by Gooch link motion and wrist plates, with automatic cut-off under governor control. Very solidly built, it gave little trouble despite the hard duty; it made 42 revolutions per wind in 65 seconds. The rope drum was 16ft in diameter and it was very fast. It remained as it was built and after 40 years of hard work it is proposed to retain it as an exhibit.

41) Crynant, Cefn Coed Colliery   SER 1316b

Type:	Horizontal double cylinder
Photo taken:	1967
Maker and Date:	Markham & Co., Chesterfield, c. 1911
Cylinder/dimensions:	32in x 5ft 0in – Drop and Corliss valves
Hp:	*Rpm:* 50 *Psi:* 160
Service:	Coal winding. Shafts 705yds. deep. Conico-cylindrical drum 13-18 feet diameter. 2½ tons coal per wind

The shafts were sunk in the early 1920s, and this engine came from the Fochriw pit which was then closed, and possibly belonged to the same company, although it was at Rhymney, well away from Cefn Coed pit. Melling's expansion cut-off gear was fitted to the inlet valves, but the drivers shut off steam at 14 of the total of 39 revolutions per wind. The tubular tail rod cover does not appear to support the tail rod. It is the standard Markham's trunk frame design, which gave little trouble, although the long wind of some 39 revolutions meant high shaft speeds in the earlier days. The No. 2 shaft engine was by Worsley Mesnes, Wigan, and supplied new to the pit in 1927. The original water-tube boilers of 1927 were later replaced by 6 of the Lancashire type with methane gas firing. There was an electrical generating plant, and a steam fan, with Belliss engines, but latterly the current was taken from the Grid, and these steam units scrapped, but steam winding was retained.

42) Crynant, Cefn Coed Colliery   SER 1316c

Type:	Horizontal double cylinder
Photo taken:	1967
Maker and Date:	Qualter Hall & Co., 1925
Cylinder/dimensions:	9ft x 1ft 0in – Slide valves
Hp: 25?	*Rpm:* 100 *Psi:* 120
Service:	Rope fitting and possibly sinking capstan

A very massive unit, this may have been made up as a capstan, with steel framing for the drum structure. The engine was a plain, slipper-guided crosshead type but unusual in that the eccentrics for driving the slide valves were placed beside the cranks inside the main bearings. It was usual to place the crankshaft bearings close to the cranks with the eccentrics on the other side of the bearings. The whole unit was so massive that it was probably a marine windlass, possibly used for cable laying, adapted, as so much was, by clever colliery engineers to pit use. It was the rope fitting capstan in 1968 and likely to remain for use.

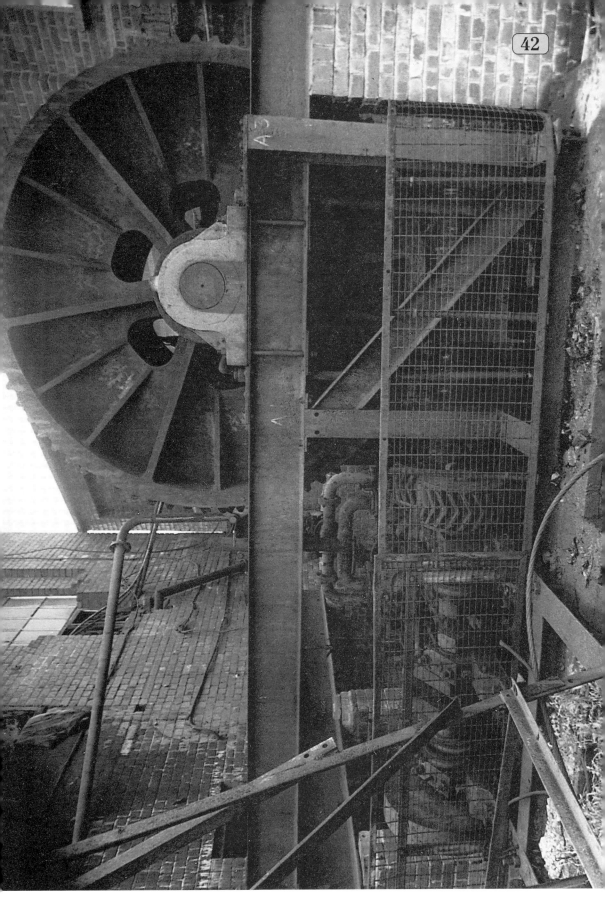

42

43) Cwm-parc, Park and Dare Collieries   SER 1310a

Type:	Horizontal double cylinder
Photo taken:	1967
Maker and Date:	Unknown, c. 1865
Cylinder/dimensions:	About 28in x 5ft 0in – Cornish valves
Service:	Coal winding. Shaft 662ft deep. Pit disused 1968

This was one of the very few engines which were installed with the winding ropes passing backwards between the two cylinders to the shaft, and in this case the engine driver sat with his back to the winding drum. The engine had been well cared for until the pits were closed, when extensive vandalism, as seen, occurred. There was no one at the colliery, and no reason for the back-to-the-shaft arrangement, opposite to the usual layout, could be given except that there was little space at the shaft top. Certainly the dirt disposal had caused problems, and here the bank had been built up on top of the original one, needing two-stage hauling. The winder was thought to have had slide valves originally, and had certainly done an immense amount of work, the collieries being very productive, but all was to be dismantled by 1970.

44) Cwm-parc, Park and Dare Collieries (The Hill Pit)   SER 1310b

Type:	Horizontal single cylinder	
Photo taken:	1967	
Maker and Date:	Llewellyn & Cubitt, Pentre, 1874	
Cylinder/dimensions:	16in x 3ft 0in – Slide valve	
Hp:	*Rpm:* 90	*Psi:* 80
Service:	Dirt haulage. Raised dirt to high level tip over original one	

This was a very old engine at the site of the older pit, latterly covered by the dirt from the later colliery workings, but with no staff there it was difficult to trace the history. The site at the top of the valley was very confined, and dirt disposal difficult, leading to very high spoil banks. The haulages were set on the top of the original pit site, the single cylinder hauling from the later shaft to the Hill pit site, and the twin cylinder hauling from there to the top, with the single boiler. It was an unusual layout in a difficult place in the head of the valley, but well served the pits, famous for their brass band and other social activities.

45) Gorseinon, Bryngwyn Steel Works   SER 944

Type:	Horizontal cross compound condensing	
Photo taken:	1958	
Maker and Date:	Galloways Ltd., Manchester, 1909	
Cylinder/dimensions:	24in and 50in x 4ft 0in – Corliss valves.	
Hp: Approx 1000	*Rpm:* 60	*Psi:* 160
Service:	Hot rolling tinplate bar. Geared drive to mills	

This was installed during the general period of increasing rolling capacity at the turn of the century, and geared to 6 mills originally. Latterly 4 more were added when ownership changed. It was interesting for the four bar crosshead guides, and heavy piston tail rod guides, and also the massive piston valve on the low pressure cylinder. The original herring-bone gear teeth in the drive had been changed to plain straight teeth in later years and the flywheel may well have been a local product. This was often done in South Wales i.e. to buy an engine without a flywheel and have one made by Price, or the Neath Abbey Foundry, or Nevilles, all of West Wales who worked very rapidly when needed. The photograph was taken in 1958 when hot rolling had ceased, although cold finishing rolling was done by electric-drive three roll stands. All was scrapped by 1963.

46) Gorseinon, Garngoch Colliery (No 3 Pit)   SER 1318

Type:	Horizontal double cylinder
Photo taken:	1967
Cylinder/dimensions:	12in x 2ft 0in and 14in x 1ft 10in – Slide valves
Service:	Was coal winding. Shaft 110yds deep

This was one of the Glazebrook group pits, but no coal was worked in the later 1960s, and No 3 was a pumping shaft only, with the engine run on compressed air, as the three boilers had been removed. There was also another shaft, which had wound coal with an electric winder. No 3 winder had completely odd sides, the engine design and the cylinder sizes being quite different, but it worked well on coal winding. It was possibly a single cylinder engine to which an odd side was added. Both sides had the slide valves on the top once, but latterly the right hand was fitted with a cylinder with the valve at the side. The drum was very small, 4ft 0in diameter, and it was doubtless very fast. When in full work there were 300 men below ground, winning some 300 tons of coal per shift.

47) Gorseinon, Grovesend Steel Works   SER 946

Type:	Horizontal, three cylinder non-condensing	
Photo taken:	1958	
Maker and Date:	Galloways Ltd., Manchester, c. 1914	
Cylinder/dimensions:	40in x 4ft 6in – Piston valves	
Hp: 6,000 (peak)	*Rpm:* 100	*Psi:* 140
Service:	Rolling steel ingots to tinplate bar	

This was typical of the massive engines which were installed with the increase of mill capacities from 1900 onwards. This was a period when South Wales was recovering from the loss of the American trade by the McKinley tariffs. A great deal of money was invested in engines such as those of SER 944 to SER 950 . The lowered costs helped to re-establish the Welsh tinplate and sheet mill trade for another half century. This was the typical Galloway's design with very light Joy's valve gear, but everywhere else very massive. It was extremely well kept, although in the mill. The colour scheme was mainly red, with green cylinders, and blue valve gear parts, so that the appearance was impressive. The handling, which was exceptional, was careful on the engine yet gave the absolute that the mill could produce in output. There were six boilers, together with a sheet mill with a vertical Corliss engine. All was scrapped about 1960.

48) Gowerton, Richard Thomas & Baldwins, Elba Steel Works SER 1301a

Type:	Horizontal double cylinder	
Photo taken:	1967	
Maker and Date:	Galloways Ltd., Manchester, 1916	
Cylinder/dimensions:	36in x 4ft 6in – Piston valves	
Hp: 4-5,000	*Rpm:* 120	*Psi:* 160

This was probably the last reversing steam-driven bar mill to be installed in South Wales, and was certainly the last to roll plate and sheet bars there. It was Galloway's standard design, non-condensing, and directly coupled to 30in roughing and finishing stands, through a Bibby flexible coupling. There had been considerable trouble with roll breakages until the Bibby coupling, which gave flexibility by driving through spring-loaded friction discs, was fitted in the 1940s. It paid its cost many times, but such couplings were very rare for the massive torques of rolling mills. The heavy stresses caused the usual failures in the foundations, and these were rebuilt later, and a cylinder cover may have been split, but such was incidental in the service. There were six Yorkshire boilers of 1916 and 1926, and this was almost certainly the only large boiler plant which had only them. (See SER 1301b)

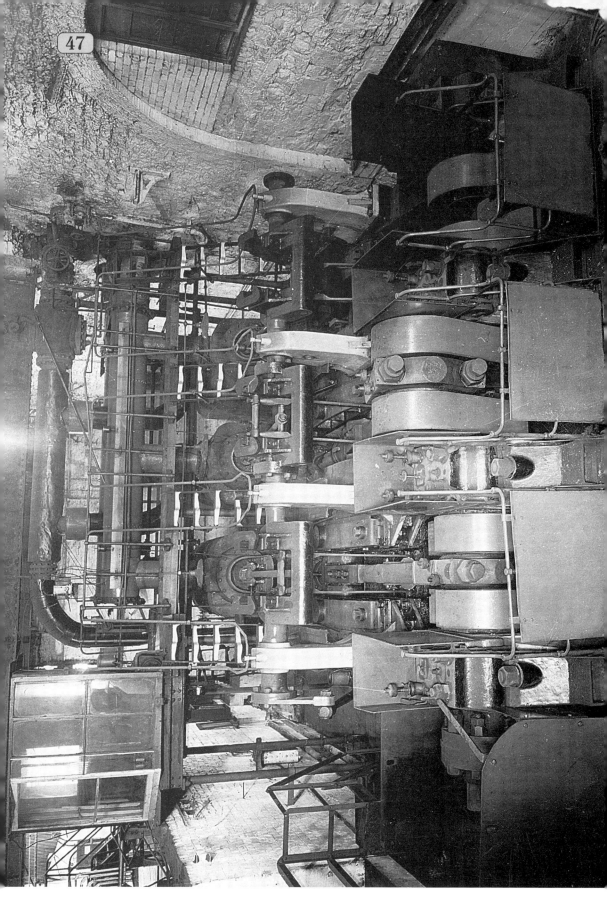

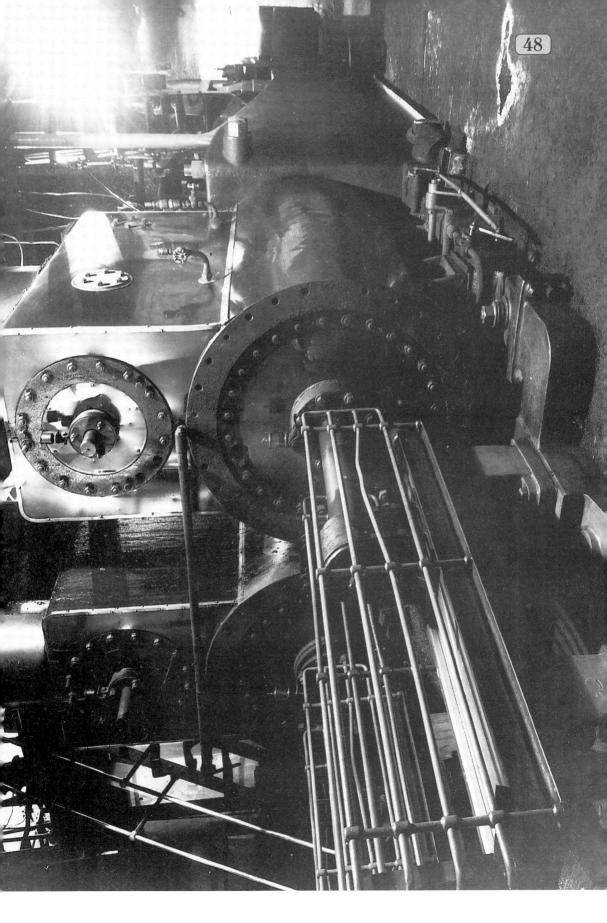

49) Gowerton, Richard Thomas & Baldwins, Elba Steel Works
SER 1301b

Type:	Six Yorkshire boilers
Photo taken:	1967
Maker and Date:	The Yorkshire Boiler Co., Bradford, 1916-26
Dimensions:	9ft 0in x 24ft 0in long – No. 4266-7-8-9 etc
Hp:	*Rpm:* *Psi:* 160

This was almost certainly the only large plant steamed entirely by Yorkshire boilers. Four were installed with the engine in 1916, and two were added in 1926, and all ran very well, driving the non-condensing engines. They still retained the original working pressure when the works ceased steel rolling in 1967. They were further used until 1972 when another concern began alloy steel rolling. The Yorkshire boiler was similar to the Lancashire, but the furnace tubes were smaller at the front and tapered to the largest diameter that the shell would accept at the rear. They made as much, if not more steam than Lancashires, although they were much shorter. They were the last development of the plain flue boiler, and gave great satisfaction; despite this there was intense opposition from the Lancashire boiler makers. These were converted to oil firing in the 1960s, but were probably scrapped with the rest of the plant in 1973. The large shell diameter, and the wide space between the flues at the front of the boiler were characteristics of the Yorkshire type.

50) Hengoed, Penallta Colliery
SER 679

Type:	Horizontal twin tandem non-condensing
Photo taken:	1954
Maker and Date:	Fraser & Chalmers, Erith, 1907
Cylinder/dimensions:	32in and 56in x 6ft – Corliss and drop valves
Hp: 2,500	*Rpm:* 35 *Psi:* 160
Service:	Coal winding. Shaft 2,250ft deep. Drum 15ft diameter

The whole colliery represented the best practice, with a highly efficient lay-out installed in an equally fine engine house complex with the colliery auxilliary plant in the centre and a very powerful winding engine at each end. There were high and low speed air compressors, and turbo generators, using all of the exhaust steam. The whole was scrapped under Nationalisation.

51) Loughor, nr Gorseinon, Bynea Steel Works
SER 948

Type:	Horizontal three crank non – condensing simple
Photo taken:	1958
Maker and Date:	Lamberton & Co., Coatbridge, Nr Glasgow, 1912
Cylinder/dimensions:	36in x 4ft 0in – Piston valves
Hp: 6,000	*Rpm:* 120 *Psi:* 160
Service:	Steel ingot rolling for tinplate and sheet bar. Direct coupled to mill

This was typical both as an example of Lamberton's design, and of the large engines installed when capacity was increased and when the tinplate trade made independent provision for its bar supplies. The mill was started by Richard Thomas & Co., who began several steel plants for bar production. The counterbalanced cast steel cranks greatly aided smooth running at the high speeds, and the engine was fitted with Allan's link motion reversing gear. As an instance of the typical duty of such engines, this reduced the open hearth steel ingot to tinplate bar 8in wide x $^1/_2$in thick in 12 passes through the roughing rolls and then - were finished in 5 passes through the finishing stand. The total time was $2^1/_2$ minutes, and the engine reversed 17 times in all, in the 120 revolutions needed.

52) Loughor, Nr Gorseinon, St David's Tinplate Works   SER 940a

Type:	Horizontal cross compound
Photo taken:	1958
Maker and Date:	D.Adamson & Co., Dukinfield, 1903
Cylinder/dimensions:	21in and 36in x 3ft 6in – Piston and slide valves
Hp: 800?	*Rpm:* 80 *Psi:* 120
Service:	Hot rolling mill. 25 rope drive

This was said to have been the first engine in South Wales to drive hot rolls by ropes, and probably drove 4 mills. Adamsons did not make many slide valve engines, and this was also interesting in that the high pressure steam cut-off control was by a radial link of the type used by Galloways, but here the main valve was piston type, with a flat slide cut-off valve working on the back of the main valve chest. The disc type cast iron cranks were also unusual for Adamsons; in fact the whole engine suggested a specially made engineer's design. The condenser was behind the low pressure cylinder and the engine ran regularly until the Musgraves cross compound Corliss valve engine of some 900 hp was installed (in 1909) which was said to have been the first to drive 6 mills directly in the South Wales tinplate trade. The plant was closed with the end of the hand tinplate mills in the late 1950s, and all scrapped.

53) Loughor, Nr Gorseinon, St. David's Tinplate Works   SER 940b

Type:	Horizontal single tandem
Photo taken:	1958
Maker and Date:	Cole, Marchent & Morley, Bradford, c. 1914
Cylinder/dimensions:	17in and 35in x 3ft 0in – Drop valves
Hp: abt 600	*Rpm:* 84 *Psi:* 160
Service:	Cold finishing rolls drive. 24 ropes to 3 tandem sets in series

It was customary to finish the sheets by cold rolling them in 3 mills, one behind the other, the sheets being fed into the first stand from which they were fed to the second and third stands automatically, the three sets being close to each other, and the sheets transferred on tables between each stand of rolls. St. David's was a progressive works, in which plant was regularly modernised, so that from a single beam engine with two mills of the 1870s it progressed to the Adamson, then the Musgrave, and finally the cold rolls were fitted with this engine which, highly economical, was also the last big addition to the plant. The mills were all scrapped when the hand mills were superseded in the 1950s.

54) Merthyr Vale, Merthyr Vale Colliery   SER 1315

Type:	Horizontal double cylinder
Photo taken:	1967
Maker and Date:	Uskside Engineering Co., Newport, 1881
Cylinder/dimensions:	14in x 2ft 0in – Slide valves
Hp: 35 – 40	*Rpm:* 100 *Psi:* 80
Service:	Capstan for changing winding ropes. Shaft 1614ft deep

This was of the type used to sink the shaft when a colliery was started, being powerful and steady working, and with the worm-geared drive, was self sustaining, all very valuable features in shaft sinking, where the safety of the sinkers in the confined space is paramount. The first shafts were sunk in 1869-1875. Electrical winding was adopted in the 1950s, and latterly this engine which had been in a brick house (which was demolished) was in the open and was to be scrapped. The shafts were some 50 yards deeper than the projected initial depth. The sinking dates, and engine date, 1881, suggest the sinking of a third shaft.

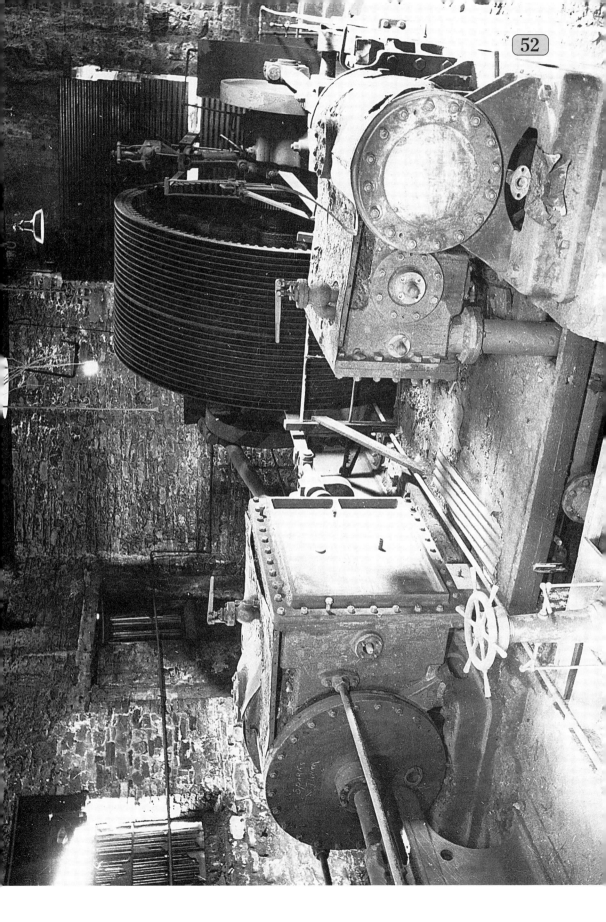

52

55) Mountain Ash, Navigation Colliery (North Pit)   SER 1304b

Type:	Double ended simple expansion non-condensing
Photo taken:	1967
Maker and Date:	The Waddle Patent Fan & Engineering Co., Llanelly, 1890s
Cylinder/dimensions:	20in x 3ft 0in – Slide valves
Hp: 120	*Rpm:* 50 *Psi:* 80
Service:	Ventilating fan and engine

Ventilation was absolutely essential in deep coal mines, and any failure stopped the pit from working, requiring the immediate withdrawal of men and horses, and great trouble in clearing gas afterwards. Therefore ventilation units were duplicated, but at Mountain Ash only the engine was doubled as, with the common colliery practice of having two engines opposed upon a single bed plate, either could drive the fan by removing the connecting rod brasses of the spare engine, and lifting the connecting rod out of the way, ready for rapid connection if needed. As usual both of the engines at Mountain Ash were placed on a long bed- plate with the connecting rods to the centre to drive on to the crankpin, although the farther engine cannot be seen. It was typical sound colliery design, very plain, with plenty of metal everywhere, and it probably needed little attention except for motion brasses during the nearly 70 years it ventilated the colliery. It is preserved, the coal being electrically wound.

56) Pontardawe, Pontardawe Alloy Sheet Works   SER 945a

Type:	Horizontal single tandem condensing
Photo taken:	1958
Maker and Date:	Cole, Marchent & Morley, Bradford, 1919
Cylinder/dimensions:	24in and 44in x 4ft 0in – Drop piston valves
Hp: 1200	*Rpm:* 90 *Psi:* 160
Service:	Hot rolling sheets. Rope drive

This was probably put in for a change to alloy rolling, needing more speed and power as it was certainly one of the most powerful sheet mills in the area. It drove by 30 ropes to a 30 ft flywheel made by Musgraves of Bolton on the rolls shaft. In every way a typical Cole, Marchent & Morley engine, it was highly economical, and operated on superheated steam, generally with little trouble, although once, the high steam temperature did melt the metallic piston rod packings, which were then changed from white metal to bronze sectors. The whole had been well maintained after the mills were closed, by the engineer seen at the stop valve, but regrettably the whole of the plant was scrapped when the hand mill process was superseded in the 1960s.

57) Pontardawe, Pontardawe Tinplate Works   SER 850c

Type:	Horizontal single tandem condensing
Photo taken:	1957
Maker and Date:	Hick, Hargreaves & Co., Bolton, c. 1910, No.1608
Cylinder/dimensions:	28in and 52in x 5ft 0in – Corliss valves
Hp: abt 750	*Rpm:* 37 *Psi:* 160
Service:	Hot rolls drive

This was fitted with a double throw crankshaft to drive mills on each side of the engine, driving directly (not through gearing) as did most of the engines installed in the early 1900s, when 4 and 6 mill engines came into use. This had always been well kept, but was scrapped with the end of the pack mill trade.

57

58) Pontardulais, Clayton Tin Plate Co.,   SER 400

Type:	Superposed compound condensing
Photo taken:	1951
Maker and Date:	Galloways, Manchester, 1902
Cylinder/dimensions:	17in and 30³/₄in x 3ft 9in – Piston valves
Hp: 420	*Rpm:* 75 *Psi:* 120
Service:	Cold roll drive

This was the standard Galloways' superposed design, and was unaltered when the plant was scrapped in 1959. It drove the usual tandem cold rolling system for finishing tinplates, by ropes from the flywheel; there were 3 sets of rolls in tandem. The hot roll engines No. 1 and 2 were made by Fodens of Sandbach (see SER 401), one of 1875, single cylinder, having been compounded later, the other built as a double crank compound about 1890.

59) Pontardulais, Glynhir Tinplate Mills   SER 942

Type:	Horizontal cross compound
Photo taken:	1958
Maker and Date:	J. Musgrave & Sons, Bolton, 1911
Cylinder/dimensions:	28¹/₂in and 50¹/₂in x 5ft 0in – Corliss valves
Hp: 1048 (1951)	*Rpm:* 30 *Psi:*
Service:	Hot rolls drive. 6 mills directly from crankshaft

A typical late direct drive this was similar to the first 6 mill engine in South Wales supplied to St. David's (SER 940), the dimensions of half a dozen engines Musgraves supplied being nearly the same. There were 3 mills on either side, and the flywheel was heavier than usual, being 32ft. in diameter. Maintenance standards as usual in the Welsh tinplate mills were very high, and Hick, Hargreaves bored the exhaust ports and supplied new valves in 1956. The boilers were Musgraves, at full pressure when 48 years old. The plant closed in 1958, but was re-opened in 1959, probably the last hand tinplate (pack) mill to work in South Wales. Finally closed early 1960s.

60) Pontypridd, Penrhiw Colliery   SER 1314

Type:	Horizontal double cylinder
Photo taken:	1967
Maker and Date:	Possibly Newbridge Foundry, Pontypridd
Cylinder/dimensions:	24in x 4ft 0in – Slide valves
Service:	Coal winding. Shaft 750ft deep. 1 tub – 30 cwt of coal per wind

Another small but heavily-used engine, this had turned up to 600 winds per shift on full coal drawing. Very plain in design, it was fitted with Gooch's link motion, and four-bar crosshead guides, but the slide valves were very unusual for the pressure relief system on the backs. It comprised a cylindrical plunger which worked on a face on the back of the slide valve, and which was adjusted by a hand wheel. It needed great care in adjusting it, but must have had good attention, as although the valve gearing was light, there appeared to have been little repair ever needed. Another unusual feature was the provision of fittings for driving, and tap connections for indicating the steam cylinders, which was rare in winding engines, the main requirement usually being that the engine should raise all the coal that could be won. From 1923 it was a pumping shaft only, and the engine ran on compressed air, as there were no boilers. It was to be preserved as almost certainly of Welsh origin.

59

61) Ponypridd, Tymawr Colliery, Hopkinstown   SER 1312a

Type:	Horizontal double cylinder
Photo taken:	1967
Maker and Date:	Barker & Cope, Kidsgrove, Staffs., 1875
Cylinder/dimensions:	36in x 6ft 0in – Drop then piston valves
Hp: ?	*Rpm:* 45 *Psi:* 80
Service:	Coal winding. Shaft 392yds deep

The history is not clear and this may have come second hand from another pit. It certainly had new cylinders by the Worsley Mesnes Co., Wigan, possibly in the 1930s. It was a heavy engine, which had given very good service on coal drawing, and in the alteration to the winding drum at various times, the single central brake track was retained. It originally had flat ropes and when round ropes were adopted, in 1909, the greater width of the drum (since the rope wraps are side by side with round ropes, whereas they wrap on top of each other if flat) led to placing the valve gear eccentrics on the outer side. The high position of the driving platform allowed the driver to see the banking, although he was in the centre of the engine. Since 1926 the shaft was used only for men and materials as a second shaft, and it was driven by compressed air from a central station.

62) Swansea, Upper Forest & Worcester Works, Morriston   SER 949

Type:	Horizontal cross compound condensing
Photo taken:	1958
Maker and Date:	Scott & Hodgson, Guide Bridge, 1908
Cylinder/dimensions:	30in and 56in x 4ft 6in – Drop and Corliss valves
Hp: 1450	*Rpm:* 90 *Psi:* 160
Service:	Steel ingot rolling to bars. Geared drive

Another example of the engines of the expansion period, this was unusual in that there were drop valves on the high pressure, with Corliss valves on the low pressure cylinders. The trunk frame was typical of Scott & Hodgson's later design and it was a massive engine in every way. Great care was taken to prevent damage to the engine when it was topped with white lead and grease to preserve the finish, and cloths to keep dust off. All was in vain, as the entire plant with another engine by Westray Copeland, and complete power house with low pressure turbine generator, and a dozen boilers was scrapped in the early 1960s.

63) Swansea, Weaver & Co., Flour Mills   SER 851

Type:	Inverted vertical triple expansion condensing
Photo taken:	1957
Maker and Date:	Wood Bros, Sowerby Bridge, 1905
Cylinder/dimensions:	18in – 28in and 42in x 4ft 0in – Corliss valves
Hp: 1200	*Rpm:* 84 *Psi:* 200
Service:	Mill drive. Ropes to several floors

This was built for Joseph Rank and installed at their Premier Mills, London. It was at work there until about 1937 when, with a new Yates and Thom engine available that could not be installed in Ireland, Ranks put the Yates into the Premier and this was moved to Swansea, where an electrical drive was proving costly. More power was needed in any case at Premier Mill. It ran well at Swansea, longer in fact than the Yates and Thom which was destroyed in the 1939 war, with most of the mill. Weaver's mills closed later when the larger dockside mills ran more cheaply, and all of the plant was almost certainly scrapped in the 1960s.

64) Swansea, Yorkshire Imperial Metals Ltd, Hafod Works, Landore
SER 962

Type:	Uniflow condensing
Photo taken:	1959
Maker and Date:	J. Musgrave & Sons, Bolton, 1910
Cylinder/dimensions:	30in x 2ft 6in
Hp: 2,000 (peak load)	*Rpm:* 110 *Psi:* 150
Service:	Non-ferrous metal rolling. Rope drive to mill

There was a beam engine house dated 1860 on the site and this was one of some dozen or more uniflows which were supplied by Musgrave, following the success and economy of the first uniflow (a Sulzer) in 1910. This engine was unique in that, although non-reversing, the rolling mill was being driven from the engine by 15 ropes to a reversing clutch which was steam operated. The load was very heavy at times, when heavy slabs of Admiralty bronze were rolled, largely for condenser tube plates, With these loads skilful operation of the steam-loaded clutch enabled the full inertia of the 20 ton engine flywheel added to that of the 50 ton wheel on the mill drive shaft, to roll the largest tube plate slabs ever cast. The mill was in use in 1972.

65) Trehafod, Lewis Merthyr Colliery
SER 959a

Type:	Horizontal double cylinder, non-condensing
Photo taken:	1959
Maker and Date:	J. Fowler and Co., Leeds, c. 1880s?
Cylinder/dimensions:	42in x 7ft 0in – Drop valves
Service:	Coal winding. Bertie shaft

There were five shafts at the pit working different coals, but nothing could be gathered on site about this. The Trevor and the Bertie pits were steam coal, and another ran to the Five Foot seam, and there was another shaft to the House coal seams. There was a large battery of Sulzer water tube boilers, to run the power house and five winders as well as the Marshall compound drop valve engine which drove the fan. There was also a double-ended slide valve engine for the older standby fan, and a large steam driven air compressor, much of which exhausted to the low pressure turbines in the power house. It was a vast complex of fine engineering in the best tradition, but very much run down with Nationalization. A fair tonnage was still mined in the 1970s; the earlier outputs were many times greater. The pit was still working in the 1970s, but the engines retained were run on compressed air from a central plant a mile away.

66) Trehafod, Lewis Merthyr Colliery
SER 959c

Type:	Horizontal double cylinder non-condensing
Photo taken:	1959
Maker and Date:	Worsley Mesnes Co., Wigan, 1910
Cylinder/dimensions:	34in x 5ft 0in – Drop and Corliss valves
Service:	Coal winding. Five Foot shaft

This was completely in contrast to the Bertie, and was Worsley Mesnes late design and, designed to use higher pressure steam, was powerful although not large. This may have exhausted to atmosphere as it was away from the power house, and possibly the standby fan also did so. It was designed to work with variable cut-off under governor control, and probably had some thirty years of work until Nationalization, but was scrapped in the early 1970s as the pit was run down. It was the latest winder on the site. The House Coal shaft winder was dated 1893.

67) Trehafod, Lewis Merthyr Colliery   SER 1313a

Type:	Horizontal opposed double cylinder
Photo taken:	1967
Maker and Date:	Union Engineering Co., Oldham, 1890s
Cylinder/dimensions:	24in x 3ft 0in – Slide valves
Hp: About 100?	*Rpm:* 60 *Psi:* 80
Service:	Ventilating fan drive by 10 ropes from flywheel

The Schiele fan was a medium speed design developed to eliminate the troubles caused by the great weight of the direct driven fans when the capacity was very large. There were two plain Meyer slide valve engines opposed upon a single long bed, which was some 35ft long, and appeared to be a single casting as no joint was visible. The lower slide bar surface for the crosshead guides was cast in one with the bed, a tribute to the builders in that they could maintain the parallel alignment in so great a length, in a vital part like the crosshead guides. It was still the standby fan in the late 1960s, and used four times a year to allow inspection of the main fan, but the engine was scrapped by 1970, when a spare electric fan was installed.

68) Trehafod, Lewis Merthyr Colliery   SER 1313b

Type:	Horizontal double cylinder
Photo taken:	1967
Maker and Date:	J. D. Leigh, Patricroft, 1893?
Cylinder/dimensions:	26in x 4ft 0in – Slide valves – Drop cut-off
Hp: ?	*Rpm:* 50 *Psi:* 80
Service:	House coal shaft winder

Another rugged Lancashire design, this had worked very heavily on the valuable House coal seam. The forked jaw type connecting rod end for the crosshead was unusual in a winding engine, and it was also interesting in that there were only two cast iron drum spiders or side discs, i.e. there was not the usual third one in the centre. The colliery had followed the usual course of development, early sinking with all steam equipment, and developing electrical and compressed air systems for coal getting around the turn of the century. This led to higher boiler pressure and with this the engines were overpowered and at the House Coal shaft, a drop cut-off valve was fitted to the valve chest inlets on each cylinder. The main boiler plant latterly was Sulzer's water tube boilers, and the electrical load was high latterly with all the haulages electrically driven, using mixed pressure generators.

69) Treharris, Deep Navigation Colliery   SER 1305

Type:	Inverted vertical double cylinder
Photo taken:	1967
Maker and Date:	Clarke, Chapman & Co., Gateshead. Early 1900s?
Cylinder/dimensions:	Abt 9in x 1ft 0in – Slide valves
Hp: ?	*Rpm:* 120 *Psi:* 80
Service:	Capstan for fitting winding ropes
	No 1 shaft. Shaft 820yds deep

The original engine for this shaft was the largest designed for winding, having cylinders 54in bore x 7ft 0in stroke, made by Fowlers of Leeds in 1888. It was replaced by an electric winder in 1921, and the smaller steam winder at No.2 was electrified in 1925. The Clarke, Chapman capstan was probably purchased from a vessel being broken up, being a marine type, with a reversing valve (not link motion) to reverse it, by interchanging the steam and exhaust passages. It is run from the compressed air supply for the coal-getting machinery underground. The capstan for No.2 shaft was entirely different, of unknown make and date, being a standard colliery haulage with double cylinders, and variable gear ratios.

70) Treherbert, Fernhill Colliery (No 3 shaft)   SER 1307

Type:	Horizontal double cylinder
Photo taken:	1967
Maker and Date:	J. & W. Leigh, Patricroft, c. 1880
Cylinder/dimensions:	28in x 5ft 0in – Slide valves
Hp: ?	*Rpm:* 50 *Psi:* 80
Service:	Coal winding. Shaft 1,131ft deep. Drum 11ft 6in diameter

This was unusual in that the makers were J. W. not the usual J. & D. Leigh, but it was a plain practical engine. The site started drawing coal from a drift mine in 1871, and later developed under Sir John Beynon and the Powell Duffryn Co., until by 1925, there were 5 shafts each with its own steam winder, an air compressor, mixed pressure turbine and alternator, with 12 boilers, and a mine. fan driven by a Belliss and Morcom triple expansion engine. Underground working was very extensive, and there were 22 haulages all steam driven at one time except for shaft inspection for the pumps. The pit was the central air compressing unit for a large area, supplying blast or compressed air for driving several winding engines where no boilers were left. An old practice, this was extensively adopted in South Wales after Nationalisation. Fernhill was to be retained as long as the blast was needed.

71) Trelewis, Taff Merthyr Colliery   SER 1306

Type:	Horizontal double cylinder
Photo taken:	1967
Maker and Date:	Maker and date unknown, 1890s?
Cylinder/dimensions:	9in x 1ft 0in – Slide valves
Hp: 25	*Rpm:* 100 *Psi:* 80
Service:	Dirt haulage to tip

Another capstan of an old design with four-bar crosshead guides. It was very heavily made with variable gear ratios, with a higher ratio for the return journeys with the empty tubs. It was regularly used as long as the pit was drawing coal and waste, but disappeared with the rest of the plant when the site was later cleared. Every colliery had at least one engine in this service, as well as rope capstans for fitting the new winding ropes, heavy lifts being a feature of colliery work. This was certainly heavily built, and quite unusual in that there were four crankshaft bearings, i.e. two between the cranks.

Monmouthshire

72) Abercarn, Abercarn Tin Plate Works   SER 850d

Type:	Uniflow condensing horizontal single
Photo taken:	1957
Maker and Date:	Hick, Hargreaves & Co., Bolton, 1924-5
Cylinder/dimensions:	26in x 3ft 0in
Hp: 500	*Rpm:* 130 *Psi:* 160
Service:	Cold rolls engine

This was one of the last uniflow engines to be installed in the tinplate mills, and drove the usual tandem three stands of cold rolls in series, by ropes off the flywheel. It was interesting in that, built with a tail piston rod, this was later removed, whereas several uniflows built without them had tail rods fitted afterwards. The works were later cleared in the general scrapping of the pack mill process. It had also had a Musgrave uniflow with a generator on the crankshaft.

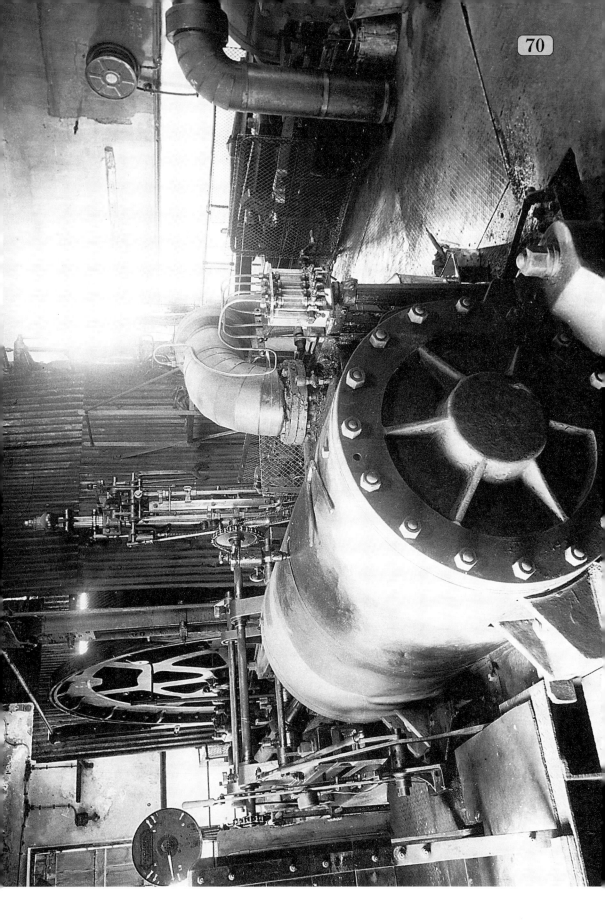

73) Abercarn, Prince of Wales Colliery   SER 85a

Type:	Vertical twin cylinder condensing
Photo taken:	1934
Maker and Date:	Unknown, c 1860?
Cylinder/dimensions:	42in x 7ft 0in – Drop valves
Hp:	*Rpm:* 25 *Psi:* 15-20
Service:	Winding engine. Shaft about 350yds deep
	Wound up to 1000 tons of coal per shift.

This had seen very heavy service in its time, since the rope reels had been stiffened. The engine itself was unaltered, unless the link motion reversing gear had replaced the plug rod type often used on vertical condensing winders. The parallel motion beams were lighter than the Durham design, and the whole appeared to be of Lancashire origin, possibly Nasmyth, Wilson. Since low pressure condensing engines and massive stone houses were less used in South Wales after 1870, this together with the use of parallel motion suggests the 1860s as a date.

74) Abercarn, South Celynen Colliery (No 1 shaft)   SER 1321a

Type:	Horizontal double cylinder
Photo taken:	1967
Maker and Date:	Fullerton, Hodgart & Barclay, Paisley, 1924
Cylinder/dimensions:	26in x 4ft 0in – Drop valves
Hp:	*Rpm:* 60 *Psi:* 140
Service:	Coal winding. Shaft 380yds deep. Rope drum 10 to
	14ft diameter

This was similar to Robey's designs in a general way and although there were many design variations in the valve gear details, it was broadly a Robey type, but with only one eccentric at each end of the cylinder. A very unusual feature was the great width between the engine centre lines, i.e. some 27ft 6in which provided over 4 feet of unsupported shaft between the bearing and the drum on each side of the drum, a feature which was usually avoided since it allowed the shaft to whip in winding. It was undoubtedly specified by the colliery when ordered, possibly with the intention of fitting a conico-cylindrical drum later, which would have needed more width. The original drum however was in use until the steam winders were replaced by electric winders early in 1971.

75) Abercarn, South Celynen Colliery (No 2 shaft)   SER 1321b

Type:	Horizontal double cylinder
Photo taken:	1967
Maker and Date:	Robey & Co, Lincoln, No 43040 and 41, 1926
Cylinder/dimensions:	About 24in x 4ft 0in – Drop valves
Hp:	*Rpm:* 60 *Psi:* 140
Service:	Coal winding. Conical-cylindrical drum. Wind made in
	40 seconds

This was Robey's standard later winding engine, with drop inlet and exhaust valves with the differential bevel gearbox reversing system on the side layshafts. It was very fast in action, and retained the trip gear under governor control, but the steam was shut off in mid-wind by the driver as well. The engine centres were 19ft 8in in this engine against the 27ft of the Fullerton, Hodgart & Barclay (SER 1321a) on No 1 shaft. The Robey had a conico-cylindrical rope drum, with three small, then three rising coils up the side to the 18 or so parallel turns on the large centre section. This was also scrapped when the electrical winders were installed in 1971.

76) Bedwellty, Llanover Colliery Pumping Shaft   SER 1497

Type:	Horizontal differential tandem compound
Photo taken:	1975
Maker and Date:	Hathorn, Davey and Co., Leeds
Cylinder/dimensions:	33in and 66in x 10ft – Piston and slide valves
Hp: About 450	*Spm:* 8-10 *Psi:* 120
Service:	Raised mine water 600ft

This was probably installed as a central pumping unit for several collieries, and Llanover was a busy colliery in the 1930s. The engine worked two-22in ram pumps, and cost £6,000 installed, being a larger example of one supplied to Bargoed. It was Davey's latest type with a single piston rod passing through the two cylinders. Metallic packing was fitted to the hp piston and valve rod glands, as the steam was superheated. It was placed in a concrete house under the pit bank, and was quite derelict in 1976, having been superseded by Sulzer vertical spindle pumps with the motors on the surface. The photograph is very poor and simply to record the pump.

77) Crumlin, Aberbeeg Colliery (South shaft)   SER 1320

Type:	Horizontal double cylinder
Photo taken:	1967
Maker and Date:	Whitaker & Low, Oldham, date unknown
Cylinder/dimensions:	22in x 4ft 0in – Slide valves
Hp:	*Rpm:* 50 *Psi:* 100
Service:	Coal winding. Shaft 150yds deep. Rope drum 10ft diameter

Aberbeeg was a very old site, the North shaft said to have been sunk in 1835, but the South was very late, i.e. about 1924, according to local opinions. It may have replaced an earlier shaft on the same site as the engine and the house were much older, more like the 1870s, than the 1920s. It was a typical plain simple colliery engine, without refinements, except the safety fittings legally required later, and even the rope drum may have been very old. Gooch reversing link motion was fitted, but the piston tail rods fitted originally had been removed, and the glands blanked off. The whole certainly appeared to be late Victorian at the latest, and was all scrapped in the late 1960s.

78) Crumlin, Navigation Colliery (South shaft)   SER 1319a

Type:	Horizontal double cylinder
Photo taken:	1967
Maker and Date:	Markham & Co, Chesterfield, 1908
Cylinder/dimensions:	About 30in x 6ft 0in – Cornish valves
Hp:	*Rpm:* 50 *Psi:* 100
Service:	Coal winding. Shaft 385yds deep

The colliery was sunk in the early 1900s, and equipped with two Markham's which, said to be new then, were of entirely different design, the South engine being of a much older type, with the Cornish valves at the side of the cylinder barrel. It could have been an old engine in stock, as few engines of this design were then being made, when higher steam pressure demanded an engine more like that at North Pit (1319b). The four-bar crosshead guides again were an old feature. Nonetheless it did a great deal of work at various times, although as the second shaft for men and materials. It was scrapped after the colliery was closed in 1967. The small size of the cylinder suggests that a new barrel for higher pressure had been fitted.

79) Crumlin, Navigation Colliery (North shaft)   SER 1319b

Type:	Horizontal double cylinder
Photo taken:	1967
Maker and Date:	Markham & Co, Chesterfield, 1907
Cylinder/dimensions:	36in x 6ft 0in – Drop and Corliss valves
Hp:	*Rpm:* 50 *Psi:*160
Service:	Coal winding. Shaft 385yds deep

This was Markham's later design, with trunk frame conico-cylindrical drum, drop inlet and Corliss exhaust valves, and very neat in every way. It had been the main coal-drawing engine, and despite the heavy useage, had needed little but routine maintenance. Gooch link reversing gear was fitted, and piston tail rods in tubular covers. The two engines represent designs some 50 years apart, yet both were very good. All was to be scrapped when the site was cleared about 1970, except one of the fan engines (SER 1319c).

80) Crumlin, Navigation Colliery (South Shaft)   SER 1319c

Type:	Horizontal four cylinder triple expansion condensing
Photo taken:	1967
Maker and Date:	Walker Bros, Wigan, c. 1907
Cylinder/dimensions:	15in – 23in - 26in and 26in x 3ft 3in – Corliss
Hp: About 500	*Rpm:* 60 *Psi:160*
Service:	Ventilating fan drive by 13 ropes off 16ft flywheel
	Walker's Indestructable fan 24ft diameter, 8ft wide

The fan power was very great, the engine being as large as a small cotton mill needed, and a similar engine was provided as standby, but later removed. The design was from the maker's middle period when many modern features were introduced, but the Corliss trip gear was the Dobson, whereas the latest Walker's had Whitehead type trip gear. This engine was still available as a standby in 1968, and was run then, and was later in charge of the National Museum of Wales, Cardiff, for removal later.

81) Ebbw Vale, Marine Colliery, Cwm   SER 684

Type:	Horizontal double cylinder
Photo taken:	1954
Maker and Date:	Nasmyth, Wilson & Co., Patricroft, No 587-8. c. 1890
Cylinder/dimensions:	41in x 6ft 0in – 4 slide valves
Service:	Coal winding. Shaft 1,242ft deep

These were said to be the most powerful in South Wales when erected in 1891, but the Harris Navigation inverted vertical cylinders were certainly larger. The Cwm engines were unusal in that there were four separate slide valves to each cylinder, i.e. one for the steam and one for the exhaust at each end, with the valve chests outside of the engine bed, which avoided difficult steam connections. The bed of one was seriously damaged when a brake track caught fire, and cold water was poured over the heated metal resulting in many cracks. The engine could not be run until Metalok stitched the worst of them with taper pin inserts, and they continued the repairs at weekends for three months, when the bed was able to carry the full load for the few years that remained before electrical winding was installed, and the steam plant scrapped.

82) New Tredegar, Elliot Colliery (West Pit)   SER 680a

Type:	Inverted vertical cross compound non- condensing
Photo taken:	1954
Maker and Date:	Andrew Barclay & Co., Kilmarnock
Cylinder/dimensions:	34in and 56in x 4ft 6in – Corliss valves
Hp: ?	*Rpm:* 30 *Psi:* 160
Service:	Coal winding. Depth 1,500ft

This was probably installed early in the 1900s, and the engine had remained little altered. The original cylindro-conical drum was changed to a 13ft 6in diameter parallel drum with a tail rope in 1958, but trouble developed with the tail rope, and this had to be removed. The engine was run with the parallel drum, but could not have been efficient – the starting load was too great. The twin tandem was all that was left at the closure.

83) New Tredegar, Elliot Colliery (East Pit)   SER 680b

Type:	Horizontal twin tandem non-condensing (built as twin cylinder)
Photo taken:	1954
Maker and Date:	Thornewill & Warham, Burton-on-Trent, 1891
Cylinder/dimensions:	42in x 6ft 0in – Drop valves as built
Hp:	*Rpm:* 20 *Psi:* 160
Service:	Coal winding. Diabolo drum 15ft to 26ft diam., i.e. conical part is at centre not ends

This was altered to tandem compound in 1904, when no doubt extensive electrification and compressed air useage developed, with the installation of Babcock & Wilcox high pressure boilers, by the makers adding Corliss valve cylinders 28in bore each side. Later, coke ovens with 750 KW generator with gas engine driven from waste gas were installed. The colliery was closed in 1967.

84) Newport, J. Lysaght & Co., Orb Works   SER 402b

Type:	Two horizontal tandem compound condensing
Photo taken:	1951
Maker and date:	Galloways, Manchester, about 1916?
Cylinder/dimensions:	34in and 64in x 6ft 0in – Corliss valves
Hp: abt 1000	*Rpm:* each 26 *Psi:* 150
Service:	Sheet mills. Hot rolls. Direct drive

These were right and left hand engines, each driving its own 6 mills with the usual roughing and finishing stands to each mill. Each of the four engines at Orb works had separate condensers and auxilliaries, but there were three boiler plants, i.e. 5 for each of the uniflow engines at the ends, with six in the middle for the two tandem engines. This was necessary in view of the great length of the mill, i.e. over 600 yards, which made it uneconomical to pipe the steam from a central boiler plant.

85) *Newport, J. Lysaght & Co., Orb Works*   SER 402c

Type:	Uniflow condensing
Photo taken:	1951
Maker and Date:	Galloways, Manchester, No. 8339, 1920
Cylinder/dimensions:	60in x 5ft 6in – Drop valves – radial valve gear
Hp: 1200	*Rpm:* 26 *Psi:* 180 and superheat
Service:	Sheet mills. Direct drive to rolls

The Orb was undoubtedly the largest sheet rolling mill in the UK, with 4 units each with six mills, all heavy duty, in a long line down the mill building. The uniflow engines which were at each end, were the largest built in the UK with the slowest speed. The last to be installed was fitted with Pilling's oil-driven valve gear, and probably installed about 1923. The loads were very variable, at times needing the whole engine power plus the effect of the 120 ton flywheels. In the above engine, the valves were operated by a link moving in a radial sector under governor control.

86) *Newport, Newport Docks Hydraulic Pumping Station*   SER 815a

Type:	Horizontal triple expansion three crank
Photo taken:	1956
Maker and Date:	J Musgrave & Sons, Bolton, 1908
Cylinder/dimensions:	28$^1/_2$in – 43in and 66in x 3ft 0in – Drop valves
Hp: About 700	*Rpm:* 40 *Psi:* 160
Service:	Hydraulic power supply for coaling hoists and general services.
	Pump rams = 7$^1/_8$in diameter

These were installed to deal with the increasing load on the hydraulic coaling tips which were extended at the time. The scheme replaced a series of small stations around the docks by two large central ones, and this engine was in the N.East station. It was Musgrave's general design, and they had supplied several similar sets with Corliss valves for an earlier plant. With the reduction in coal shipping, they were less used after 1950, and electric pumps replaced the steam sets which were scrapped about 1959. The air pump was driven off the high pressure crank pin.

87) *Newport, Newport Docks Hydraulic Pumping Station*   SER 815c

Type:	Horizontal triple expansion three crank
Photo taken:	1956
Maker and Date:	Galloways Ltd., Manchester, 1914
Cylinder/dimensions:	28$^1/_2$in – 45in and 70in x 3ft 0in – Drop valves
Hp: About 700	*Rpm:* 40 *Psi:* 160
Service:	Hydraulic power supply for coaling hoists and general services.
	1,250 gpm to 830 psi for general hydraulic load
	Accumulator 20in x 20ft stroke

These were very similar to the Musgrave sets and possibly all were made to the docks engineer's designs, each having bucket and plunger pumps driven off the piston tail rods. There were few differences in performance or layout, again being superseded in the general re-organisations of the 1950s. The power station for the Galloways also included the docks generating plant of two 500 KW generators, and the plant was served by six Lancashire boilers with superheaters, and a 200 ft high brick chimney.

88) Newport, Stewarts & Lloyds Ltd, Mannesmann Tube Works SER 811

Type:	Two horizontal twin tandem condensing
Photo taken:	1956
Maker and Date:	Cole, Marchent & Morley, Bradford, 1917
Cylinder/dimensions:	23in and 44in x 5ft 0in – Drop piston valves
Hp: 2,500	*Rpm:* 85 *Psi:* 180
Service:	Hot tube forming mill drives

These are identical engines, one driving the piercing, and the other the pilgrim follower rolls, which formed the pierced billets to tubes. Each drove by 42 ropes – the piercing mill at 57-75 rpm, and other mill ran at 45-65 rpm, with mill shaft flywheels of 80 and 120 tons weight. They were steamed by Babcock and Wilcox boilers with superheaters and the whole plant was very well maintained, and fully loaded in 1972. The guaranteed steam rate for the engines originally was $10^{1}/_{2}$ lbs. of steam per indicated horsepower hour.

89) Pontypool, Glyn Pit   SER 812

Type:	Vertical single cylinder
Photo taken:	1956
Maker and Date:	Neath Abbey Ironworks, c. 1845
Cylinder/dimensions:	36in x 5ft 0in – Drop valves
Hp:	*Rpm:* 30 *Psi:* 60
Service:	Coal winding. Flat ropes. Shaft 220yds deep

Although a small hillside mine, Glyn produced many thousands of tons of coal in some 90 years as an active pit, i.e. to 1937. There was the one single cylinder winder only and the pump was a single cylinder beam engine geared to the well rods in another shaft. Originally the headgear appears to have been of the tandem type, one cage possibly travelling in the pump shaft. It was said that the valves of the winding engine had been hand operated for many years, i.e. not attached to the eccentrics. It was a pity that this last Welsh early mining winder and pump in situ could not have been saved. They were to have been scrapped in 1972, all the brasses having been stolen, but the engines have been left, slowly deteriorating – for years the only plant on the site.

90) Pontypool, Partridge, Jones & John Paton Ltd, Pontnewynydd
                                                                              SER 961

Type:	Two horizontal tandem condensing
Photo taken:	1959
Maker and Date:	Hick, Hargreaves and Co, Bolton, 1910
Cylinder/dimensions:	35in and 65in x 6ft 0in – Corliss valves
Hp: 1300	*Rpm:* 32 *Psi:* 150
Service:	Sheet rolling mill drives

These were said to have driven 8 mills off each engine at one time, directly connected to the crankshaft, and driven off to the right and the left, each set of engines and mills being completely independent. They were almost the largest in the sheet trade in South Wales, but latterly much less used as the sheet trade fell off. The cold rolls were also steam driven until 1948, when motors were installed for this load. There were 10 Lancashire boilers of various makes, three of which would drive one of the tandem hot rolls. The flywheels were 32ft diameter. All was scrapped with the development of the strip rolling process, and the works let to other tenants. The engines were typical of Hicks in every way.

89

91) Pontypool, Pontypool Tin Plate Works – Central Works   SER 852

Type:	Horizontal side-by-side condensing
Photo taken:	1957
Maker and Date:	Galloways Ltd., Manchester, 1914?
Cylinder/dimensions:	24in and 48in x 4ft 0in – Corliss valves
Hp: 600	*Rpm:* 30 *Psi:* 140
Service:	Hot rolls drive; direct to mills

This engine had a chequered career, since, built for another works, it lay in packing cases until 1926, when it was installed at this site. Even then its adventures had not finished since it was soon fitted with new cylinders, possibly slightly larger, by Hick, Hargreaves. No reason was known for the change, as the works were storage only in later years, but it had been well used for some years. The mills were scrapped in the 1950s. The four-bar guides were unusual for a non-reversing engine. The cold roll engine was made by Marsden's, Heckmondwike; it was a tandem.

92) Pontypool, Tirpentwys Colliery   SER 685

Type:	Inverted vertical twin cylinder non-condensing
Photo taken:	1954
Maker and Date:	Daglish and Co., St Helens, 1905
Cylinder/dimensions:	40in x 6ft 0in – Drop valves
Hp:	*Rpm:* 30 *Psi:* 120
Service:	Coal winding. Parallel drum

Inverted vertical winders were uncommon, but the type was adopted here due to lack of room behind the engine, the house being almost cut into the rock face behind. It probably replaced a vertical with overhead crankshaft, but no history of this was known. It was said to have been made with drop valves, which were replaced by Corliss possibly with new cylinders later. The colliery had a power house but this was scrapped and later the whole was converted to electric driving, finally being linked by a drift to Hafodyrynys New Mine the other side of the mountain.

93) Pontypool, Town Forge   SER 853

Type:	Horizontal side-by-side compound
Photo taken:	1957
Maker and Date:	Galloways Ltd., Manchester, 1890
Cylinder/dimensions:	26in and 46in x 4ft 0in – Slide valves
Hp: 600	*Rpm:* 30 *Psi:*140
Service:	Hot rolls drive: direct to mills

This was the pure Galloways hot rolls engine design, of which they sent at least 25 to the South Wales mills by 1903. There were 3 slide valves, one for admission to the high pressure cylinder, one between the cylinders to transfer the steam directly to the low pressure, with an exhaust valve for the low pressure cylinder. (SER 852 was the same when built). The cranks were at slightly less than 180 degrees apart, and this engine remained exactly as built, retaining Galloways governor controlled cut-off gear, and parabolic governor. This had probably driven mills on both sides, with a very heavy flywheel. It had good maintenance, including valve refacing in the early 1950s, but all was scrapped with the end of the pack mill tinplate trade.

94) Portskewett, G.W.R., Sudbrook Pumping Station   SER 847a

Type:	Six Cornish beam pumps
Photo taken:	1956
Maker and Date:	Harvey and Co., Hayle, 1887
Cylinder/dimensions:	70in x 10ft 0in
Hp:	*Spm:* 6-8 *Psi:* 40
Service:	No 1 engine house, pumping from the 29ft shaft

No 1 house with three engines on either side of the well was unique, since all were identical as engines (although the pumps differed) and were installed new as a single order, to control the inflow from the Great Spring. Twelve Lancashire boilers were installed for these six engines. The engines were never idle at any time until replaced by electrically driven pumps in 1963. All were then scrapped.

95) Portskewett, G.W.R., Sudbrook Pumping Station   SER 847b

Type:	Six Cornish beam pumps
Photo taken:	1956
Maker and Date:	Harvey and Co., Hayle, 1887
Cylinder/dimensions:	70in x 10ft 0in
Hp:	*Spm:* 6-8 *Psi:* 40
Service:	No 1 engines. Beam loft

The engines were unusual for Cornish designs in that the beams were built up of steel plates rivetted together, whereas the Cornish standard was cast iron beams. The cylinders were set wider apart than the pump rod centres, with the inner beam in line but with the outer two beams at an angle to the centre one, which gave more room around the cylinders; the pumps were notably close together in the well, some 180ft below.

96) Portskewett, G.W.R., Sudbrook Pumping Station   SER 847c

Type:	Two Bull type
Photo taken:	1956
Maker and Date:	Harvey & Co., Hayle, 1878
Cylinder/dimensions:	50in x 10ft 0in
Hp:	*Spm:* 6-8 *Psi:* 40
Service:	"Iron Shaft" pumping engines

These were the first pumping engines installed on the site, and were later assisted by the 75in engine installed to pump from the same shaft, the latter being the only engine on the site larger than 70in bore. The Bull engines were largely standby in later years, the Great Spring requiring the capacity of the No.1 House. The flow was never less than 13 million gallons per day and over 35 millions in wet seasons. Two of the Bull engines were to be saved.

97) Portskewett, G.W.R., Sudbrook Pumping Station   SER 847d

Type:	Horizontal single tandem compound condensing
Photo taken:	1956
Maker and Date:	Walker Brothers, Pagefield Ironworks, Wigan, 1923
Hp:	*Rpm:* 40 *Psi:* 140
Service:	Engine driving tunnel ventilation fan

The fan and engine was replaced in 1923, when not only was the original worn after 40 years nonstop working, but also with the increasing train load more ventilation was essential. The engine was fitted with Doerfel valve gear with twin side shafts, and was very economical. It ran without incidents until the station was electrified when the fan was retained, but the drive was taken by electric motors, two being provided in case of breakdown, driving by vee belts to the fan shaft.

Montgomeryshire

98) Llanidloes, Hamer's Leather Works   SER 656

Type:	Horizontal cross compound condensing
Photo taken:	1954
Maker and Date:	Daniel Adamson & Co, Dukinfield, 1884
Cylinder/dimensions:	15in and 22in x 3ft 0in – Wheelock valves
Hp: 100	*Rpm:* 100 *Psi:* 100
Service:	Factory drive. 20in leather belt

This was one of the earliest Wheelock engines which Adamsons made, after taking up the licence in 1884. It was a complete copy of the American design, and ran regularly until replaced by electrical drives in 1954, with no alterations and few repairs. It was not over-loaded, was economical, but was broken up some years later. A new Adamson boiler (No.7933) for 100 psi was installed in 1919, and supplied process steam after the engine was scrapped. It was fitted with the type "A" Wheelock valve design with separate plugs for the inlet and exhaust valves.

Cheshire

99) Birkenhead, Mersey Docks & Harbour Board Workshops SER 101

Type:	Single rotative beam non-condensing
Photo taken:	1935
Maker and Date:	Geo Forrester and Co, Vauxhall Foundry, Liverpool. Date?
Cylinder/dimensions:	20in x 3ft 6in – Slide valve
Hp: 20-25	*Rpm:* 48 *Psi:* 60
Service:	Main drive to shafting by bevel wheels and an inclined shaft

This was placed beside the boiler in a house adjoining the workshops. The Cornish boiler provided steam for the engine, the steam hammer in the forge, and the Roots blower for the foundry cupola. The engine was of the sturdy design characteristic of the mid 19th century and ran virtually trouble free for over half a century. It was the short stroke industrial counterpart of the slighter waterworks engines of the period 1850-1880.

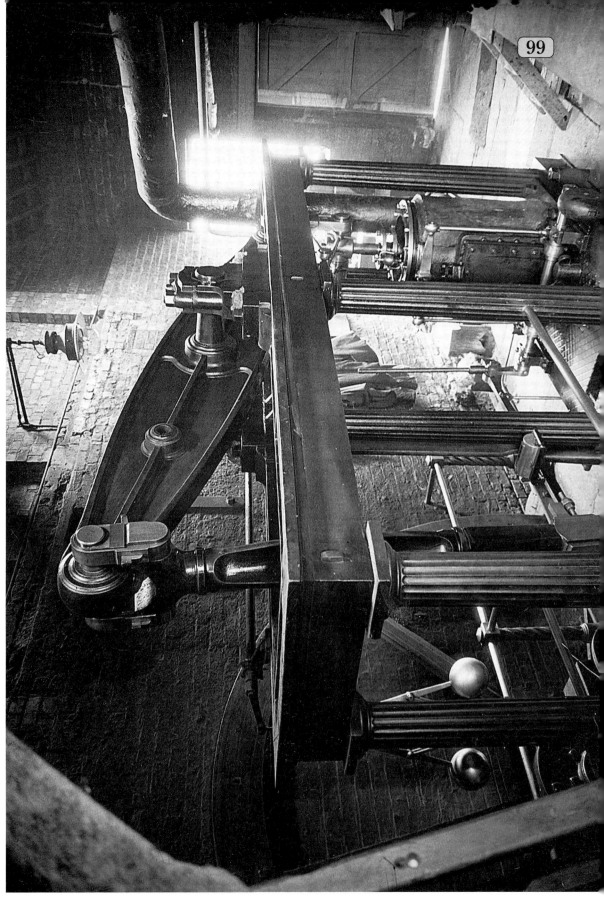

100) Birkenhead, Mersey Railway Co., Shore Rd Pumping Station
SER 260

Type:	Compound grasshopper pumps non-rotative
Photo taken:	1939
Maker and Date:	A. Barclay & Co., Kilmarnock, c1882.
Cylinder/dimensions:	36in x 10ft 0in stroke 55in x 13ft 0in stroke – Drop valves
Hp: ?	*Spm:* 6-8 *Psi:* 70
Service:	Tunnel pumps. Lift 90ft 0in, 40in plungers – 15ft stroke
	Beams 32ft 6in long

These were the heaviest pumps made by Barclays, the total weight being 260 tons. The main pump rods were of oak with a crosshead and guides just below the surface and with a balance beam to offset the excess weight of the rods. The pumps were driven from the ends of the beams, so, having a longer stroke. There were originally 11 Lancashire boilers to drive the engines and probably the fans, but these were replaced by Stirling water tube ones when electric traction was introduced. Sulzer electric pumps were installed at the bottom of the shaft in the late 1920s, but the Barclays were used at times until 1950.

101) Birkenhead, Mersey Railway Co., Power Station, Shore Rd SER 468

Type:	Inverted vertical cross compound condensing
Photo taken:	1952
Maker and Date:	Westinghouse, Pittsburgh, USA, c. 1899.
Cylinder/dimensions:	30in and 60in x 4ft 0in – Drop valves (hp Cylinder)
	Corliss valves (lp)
Hp: 1600	*Rpm:* 85 *Psi:* 160
Service:	Electricity generating. D C for traction

These were some of the many American units which came here about the turn of the century. Standing 27ft. high and some 40ft. across, they were impressive in size and did good work until superseded by the turbines, but they were retained as standby until all of the current was taken from the Grid in the 1960s. The engines generated 1,250kw each. The railway performed a useful service, giving transport when fogs made the ferries unreliable.

102) Birkenhead, West Cheshire Water Board, Prenton Pumping Station
SER 258

Type:	Cornish beam
Photo taken:	1938
Maker and Date:	Harvey & Co, Hayle, 1880
Cylinder/dimensions:	60in x 8ft 0in
Service:	Town supply from well. Pump 140ft down, 18in bucket –
	8ft stroke
	Beams 30ft long

This was the standard Harvey engine of the end of the Cornish engine era. Two surface lift pumps were fitted, but it had been used very little after the Lilleshall sets (see SER 1003) were installed. The parallel motion was fitted inside of the beam flitches and the "C" collar crosshead fixing, with supporting webs for the gudgeon pins, were features of Cornish design.

103) Birkenhead, West Cheshire Water Board, Prenton Pumping Station
SER 1003

Type:	Two horizontal single tandem condensing
Photo taken:	1959
Maker and Date:	The Lilleshall Co., Oakengates, 1923
Cylinder/dimensions:	26in and 54in x 4ft 0in – Corliss valves
Hp: 300	*Rpm:* 20 *Psi:* 160
Service:	Town supply from wells. Well and surface pumps driven from tail rod

These replaced the Harvey Cornish beam engine at the site, which pumped 1 million gallons to similar heads. The Lilleshalls each pumped 2,400,000 gallons per day and used 8.3 cwts. coal per hour. The well was 280ft. deep, and there was a single bucket pump to each engine in the well, and there were four surface ram pumps for the Heswall and the Prenton areas with heads of 350 and 210ft respectively. One engine was worked at a time, usually for twelve months on end. Two Daniel Adamson boilers were supplied with the engine, and the whole gave little trouble until electrically driven turbine pumps were installed in the early 1960s, and the steam plant scrapped.

104) Bollington, The Bleachers Association, Ingersley Vale   SER 257

Type:	Waterwheel *The Belle of the Vale*
Photo taken:	1938
Maker and Date:	Unknown
Cylinder/dimensions:	57ft 0in diameter, 7ft 0in wide
Service:	Plant drive. Gear ring 54ft. Pinion 5ft 0in diameter

This was later used to drive a dynamo, by a belt from the third motion shaft, but originally had driven long shafting runs to the scattered works. There were also two or three small steam engines or the outer parts. The arms of the wheel were fitted with threads and nuts at the end, and the rim was in 28 sectors, one per arm. The buckets were not ventilated, but the hatch to feed the water was curved, and fed the water over the top to use the highest head.

105) Bredbury, nr. Stockport, Pear New Mill   SER 494

Type:	Double Manhattan
Photo taken:	1952
Maker and Date:	George Saxon Ltd., Openshaw, Manchester, 1913
Cylinder/dimensions:	30in & 60in x 4ft 6in – Drop H P – Corliss valves
Hp: 4,000	*Rpm:* 77 *Psi:* 165
Service:	Cotton spinning. 140,000 mule spindles in 1914 40-80s count

The mill was planned as a double mill which would have needed 4,000 h.p. to drive both halves. The second half was, however, never completed, so the left hand side of the engine was not used. The engine regularly carried 1,850 h.p. and often 2,000 h.p. on the one crank, with three boilers in steam. The flywheel was almost certainly the widest in a cotton mill, i.e. with 73 rope grooves and, 15ft. wide, comprised three separate wheels close together upon the shaft, and was 24ft. diameter. In contrast to the American Manhattans the high pressure cylinder was horizontal. It was 28ft. high and 41ft. long, and was scrapped when the mill was converted to electrically driven ring frames in the 1960s.

106) Brereton, nr. Holmes Chapel, Flour Mill   SER 1167

Type:	Horizontal single cylinder condensing
Photo taken:	1964
Maker and Date:	Edwin Foden, Sandbach, date unknown
Cylinder/dimensions:	12in x 2ft 0in – Slide valve
Hp: abt 30	*Rpm:* 80 *Psi:* 60?
Service:	Assisted water wheel

This was the last small Foden engine remaining, and it was hoped to preserve it. It was connected to a middle breast water wheel 19ft diameter by 6ft 3in wide, by a jaw clutch, and drove directly to the millstone driving shaft, to which the water wheel was connected by double increasing gearing of about 9 to 1 total ratio. There was a single Cornish boiler possibly also by Fodens, about 20ft x 5ft diameter. The plant was long disused in the 1960s, but preserved in good order, in a dry place. The water wheel can be seen through the aperture in the wall at the side of the engine, and there were four pairs of flour grinding stones each 4ft 6in diameter. It is possible that the condenser was an addition to a stock design of small factory type engine that Mr.Foden produced early in the works history.

107) Compstall, nr. Marple, Calico Printers Association, Compstall Mill SER 808

Type:	Horizontal cross compound condensing
Photo taken:	1956
Maker and Date:	Daniel Adamson, Dukinfield, 1884
Cylinder/dimensions:	21in and 36in x 4ft 0in
Hp: abt 800	*Rpm:* 75 *Psi:* 160
Service:	Cotton weaving. Rope drive. Also water turbines 600 and 240 hp

The extensive water power was regularly used to the 1960s, the turbines and the engine each driving by ropes to the alternators from which the looms were driven by electric motors. The site had long been noted for the available water power and it was used as long as weaving was carried on at the site, possibly ceasing with the trade re-organisation of the late 1960s. The engine was originally fitted with Wheelock valves when built, Adamsons having just taken out a licence for this, but the high pressure was replaced by a Good-fellows Corliss cylinder in the late 1890s; the early history was however obscure. It had the last remaining set of Ramsbottoms folding trip gear, on the high pressure cylinder.

108) Dukinfield, Bowker and Ball & Co., Tame Valley Mill   SER 1142

Type:	Inverted vertical compound
Photo taken:	1963
Maker and Date:	Scott & Hodgson, c. 1904
Cylinder/dimensions:	18in and 40in x 3ft 6in – Corliss and piston valves
Hp: 800	*Rpm:* 85 *Psi:* 160
Service:	Cotton spinning

The mill was built in 1853, originally with a beam engine and gear drives, and the Scott and Hodgson was placed in a house outside of the mill, giving good length for the rope drives. It was a plain, simple, but reliable and economical unit, and served very well, supplying all of the power until some 60 years later. Then, replacement of the mule spindles by ring spinning frames reduced the load, as the new frames were motor driven. The engine was almost identical with the one at Grosvenor Mill (SER 711), but this engine was said to have been dispatched from Scott's works without prior assembly in the erecting shop. The low pressure piston valve had inside admission, and the exhaust pipe was in the

Continued on page164...

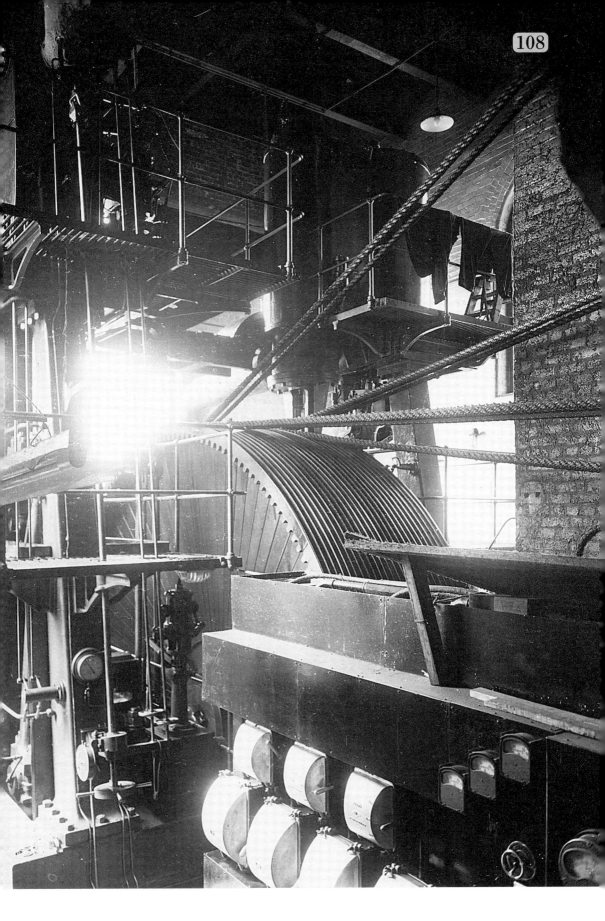

Continued from page 160...

line of the upper platform which was swept upwards to clear it. The engine was scrapped when electrical drive ring frames were fully installed, all of the spinning mules also being scrapped except one which was presented to Manchester Science Museum.

109) Dukinfield, Park Road Spinning Co.,   SER 638

Type:	Horizontal four cylinder triple expansion
Photo taken:	1954
Maker and Date:	Benjamin Goodfellow, Hyde, 1893
Cylinder/dimensions:	21in – 35in and 2 x 40in x 5ft 0in – Corliss valves
Hp: 1600	*Rpm:* 63$^1/_2$ in *Psi:* 190
Service:	Cotton spinning. Drive by 46 ropes

Park Road was one of the best kept mills in the trade; even the basement, usually dark and oily, being bright and white-washed. The original Ramsbottom valve gear was replaced by G. Saxons after numerous failures of the steel tripping cranks. The mill was very efficient, producing up to 90,000 lbs of yarn per week on 53 tons of coal. Motor-driven ring frames replaced steam and mule spinning in the 1950s when the engine was scrapped. This also had a Lumb governor fitted in later years.

110) Dukinfield, Queen Mill Co.,   SER 714

Type:	Inverted vertical triple expansion
Photo taken:	1955
Maker and Date:	Scott & Hodgson, Guide Bridge, 1902
Cylinder/dimensions:	21in – 35in – 57in x 4ft 6in – Corliss and piston valves
Hp: 1600	*Rpm:* 80 *Psi:* 160
Service:	Cotton spinning

Scott & Hodgson's triples although generally similar had slight differences, and in this one, the middle cylinder was fitted with twin forged steel front columns and the low pressure cylinder had two piston valves. It ran successfully until cotton spinning was stopped, and when the mill closed it was occupied by a foam rubber manufactory. An explosion in this damaged the chimney later.

111) Ellesmere Port, Manchester Ship Canal Docks,
Hydraulic Power Houses   SER 1328

Type:	Double cylinder pumping non-condensing
Photo taken:	1968
Maker and Date:	Armstrong, Whitworth, Elswick, No 227
Cylinder/dimensions:	12in x 1ft 3in – Slide valves
Hp: ?	*Rpm:* 30 *Psi:* 80
Service:	Hydraulic power supply for lock gates, capstans, etc

Although late (i.e. current with the construction of the Manchester Ship Canal) these were the most simple plants, with non-condensing engines, exhausting to a feed water heater. There were two stations, each similar with the engines back to back, and the pump rams in line with the piston rods, with pitchfork type connecting rods straddling the pump barrels. There was also a Gwynne's low lift pump for the fresh water supply (since no water was returned to the hydraulic system), and these pumps also pumped water into the Ellesmere canal system to maintain the level there. There had been two boilers for the older side, and once four more for the later one containing the Gwynne's impounding pumps. There was also a Pearn's type vertical pump just visible, which also fed raw water to the hydraulic system.

112) Hyde, Ashton Bros., Carrfield Mill   SER 606b

Type:	Horizontal cross compound condensing
Photo taken:	1953
Maker and Date:	Benjamin Goodfellow, Hyde, 1890, No 849 & 850
Cylinder/dimensions:	26in and 50in x 6ft 0in – Corliss valves
Hp: 1400	*Rpm: 52* *Psi: 160*
Service:	Cotton spinning. Flywheel 32ft diameter. 36 ropes

This had remained unaltered with the original valve gear, which was the Goodfellows block type and which usually gave little trouble. The mill was largely electrically driven when the photograph was taken, the load being mainly initial preparation of opening and carding on the lower floors. All steam drives were replaced by 1960.

113) Hyde, Slack Mills Co. (No 4 Mill), Queen St   SER 605

Type:	Horizontal cross compound condensing
Photo taken:	1953
Maker and Date:	Daniel Adamson & Co., Dukinfield, 1889
Cylinder/dimensions:	20in and 38in x 4ft 6in – Wheelock valves
Hp: 500	*Rpm: 62* *Psi: 120*
Service:	Weaving shed. Gear drive

Daniel Adamson began making Wheelock valve engines under licence about 1884, and built them for all services, the largest cylinders being for the Globe Spinning Co., Slaithwaite and the steel works at East Moors, Cardiff (1890s). The Slack engine was the purely American design with trunk frame, and the steam stop valve beneath the high pressure cylinder. The guide trunk was a single casting joined to the main bearing by a flange with no support beneath the guides. It worked steadily, unaltered, until all was electrically driven, the whole concern closing about 1960, when all was scrapped.

114) Kettleshulme, Sheldon Bros., Lumb Hole Hill   SER 1189a

Type:	Single cylinder beam engine
Photo taken:	1965
Maker and Date:	Unknown, possibly 1840s
Cylinder/dimensions:	21in x 4ft 0in – Slide valve
Hp: 50-60?	*Rpm: 35?* *Psi: 30*
Service:	Candle wick manufacture. Assisted waterwheel

The little mill right out in the country had probably stopped working in the 1930s after nearly a century at work, in a specialised branch of the cotton trade. It was a very early cotton and corn milling site, and mainly depended on water power; the steam side was never run if possible. The only known major work on the beam engine was a new cylinder supplied by Arnfield, Engineers, New Mills, date unknown. It was coupled into the water wheel drive by sliding the pinion on the crankshaft to engage it with the large pinion seen between the flywheel arms, which was fixed to the mill driving shaft. The boiler was a Cornish type, too small to fire internally, so it was set over the fire, as a return tube setting.

113

GOLD MEDAL LONDON
1885
GOLD MEDAL EDINBURGH
1886
AUTOMATIC ENGINE
WHEELOCKS PATENT
DANIEL ADAMSON & Cº
ENGINEERS
DUKINFIELD
— 1889 —

115) Kettleshulme, Sheldon Bros., Lumb Hole Hill   SER 1189b

Type:	High breast water wheel
Photo taken:	1965
Maker and Date:	Unknown
Cylinder/dimensions:	25ft diameter x 6ft 0in wide
Hp: 30-40?	*Rpm:* *Psi:*
Service:	Main mill drive by internal toothed gear ring

This was the main power source, and may be of the 1820-30s as it has the early type of cotter fitting for holding the arms into the hubs. The buckets had rusted away, but the radial and diagonal arms were still quite sound as was the rim shroud structure. There was a single drive, by the internal toothed sectors to a pinion 2½ft diameter and thence to the mill by spur and bevel gears. The mill once had upper floors, but these were damaged by fire, when the mill was let to other users in recent years. The little place and power plant remained intact otherwise in the 1960s.

116) Malpas, Mr Stevenson   SER 689

Type:	Two Russian Fowler ploughing engines, No 14942-14962
Photo taken:	1954
Service:	Cable ploughing

These were similar to SER 686 at Bucknell, Shropshire and the details apply to these.

117) Marple, Goyt Mill   SER 640

Type:	Horizontal cross compound
Photo taken:	1954
Maker and Date:	Carels Frères, Ghent, 1905
Cylinder/dimensions:	36½in and 63in x 5ft 3in – Drop valves
Hp: 2500	*Rpm:* 70 *Psi:* 150 superheated
Service:	Cotton spinning

This again illustrates the very high finish of the mills fitted with Carels engines in the early 1900s. The load was very heavy comprising ring and mule spinning for the heaviest counts, demanding high power and ready ability to accept overload. The Carels engine did this regularly, and the mill was successful, but it was closed in the reduction of surplus spindles scheme in the 1960s. The lighting plant was in the alcove at the left.

118) Preston Brook, Bridgewater Canal Warehouses   SER 98

Type:	Single condensing beam
Photo taken:	1935
Maker and Date:	Bridgewater Trust, 1849
Cylinder/dimensions:	16½in x 3ft 0in – Slide valve
Hp: 10-12	*Rpm:* 20-25 *Psi:* 20
Service:	Drives for warehouse hoists and wharf cranes
	Beam 10ft 0in long. Flywheel 11ft 0in diameter

There were two similar warehouses, each with its own plant. The drives were taken by bevel wheels to vertical shafts for the hoists and by underground shafts to the cranes which were on the canal wharf. The main shafting worked continuously, the hoists and cranes each having its own clutch for independent use. The whole was a good example of early engineering and in 1935 probably the only remaining example of such a layout.

119) Romiley, Elder Mill Co.,   SER 728

Type:	Inverted vertical compound condensing
Photo taken:	1955
Maker and Date:	Daniel Adamson & Co, Dukinfield, 1907?
Cylinder/dimensions:	abt 18in and 36in x 3ft 6in – Wheelock valves
Hp: 400	*Rpm:* 105 *Psi:* 160
Service:	Cotton spinning

This was probably the only vertical Wheelock valve engine in cotton spinning, although there were two or three horizontal Wheelocks in the trade. This was a fast-running engine in a small engine room and may well have replaced a smaller one, as the mill may have once been in a different trade. The Adamson boiler was 1908, and, this suggests a change of plant then. The Wheelock was a short stroke sliding valve, each separate for the steam and the exhaust functions, and mounted upon a separate plug which, with the valves, could be removed from the cylinder. Spare blocks were kept and were readily inserted, enabling high efficiency to be maintained without interrupting the running of the mill. A new low pressure cylinder was later fitted by Scott and Hodgson. The mill closed in 1964.

120) Stalybridge, Robert Broadbent & Co., Engineers   SER 897

Type:	Horizontal side-by-side compound
Photo taken:	1958
Maker and Date:	T. Wainwright & Sons, Engineers, Stalybridge
Cylinder/dimensions:	12in and 21in x 2ft 0in – Corliss and slide valves
Hp: 80	*Rpm:* 90 *Psi:* 150
Service:	Works drive. 7 ropes

This ran virtually unaltered until the works were converted to electric drives about 1960. Nothing was known of the original engine at the works, but this was very compact. The high pressure crank was interesting as there was a bearing in the half crank from the low pressure side, the flywheel being driven by a crankpin working in brasses in the low pressure side crank. This gave flexibility in the drive and bearings, and avoided the trouble which occurred when the outboard bearing of the crankshaft wore down, frequently fracturing the crankshaft in the outer web. The flywheel was in halves, with a bolted hub joint, with rings shrunk on. The arms were never boarded in.

121) Stalybridge, Quarry Street Mill   SER 690

Type:	Horizontal cross compound condensing
Photo taken:	1954
Maker and Date:	T. Wainwright & Sons, Stalybridge, 1899
Cylinder/dimensions:	21^1/$_2$in and 41in x 4ft 0in – Corliss and slide valves
Hp: 750	*Rpm:* 80 *Psi:* 160
Service:	Cotton spinning

This was known as *Old Ben's* engine, since Ben Wainwright designed it when he was 19 years old. Named *Frederick* and *Arthur* by the management, it was a very good engine which, usually fully loaded, required little repair. In fact the Lumb governor fitted later was probably the greatest expense involved. The mill suffered in the poor trade of the 1950s and, after a run of part-time working, was closed when all was scrapped. This drove backwards as well as forward. It is interesting that despite their very wide repute for sound work, and ability to do any repair, Wainwrights built very few large engines.

122) Stalybridge, Stalybridge Spinning Co.,   SER 877

Type:	Horizontal twin tandem compound condensing
Photo taken:	1957
Maker and Date:	B. Goodfellow, Hyde, c. 1883
Cylinder/dimensions:	17^1/$_2$in and 40^1/$_2$in x 6ft 0in – Corliss and slide valves
Hp: 1900	*Rpm:* 56 *Psi:* 180
Service:	Cotton spinning. 27 rope drive. 30ft flywheel

The engine was built as a twin tandem compound, but never equalled the performance of the Castle Mill which had a Yates and Thom triple expansion (scrapped when the mill was closed in 1936). The Stalybridge engine was rebuilt twice in attempting to improve the economy, once by Yates and Thom (1910) and by Scott and Hodgson (1921), and Scotts also fitted a new crankshaft with their tangential keys, replacing the original staked shaft and wheel which was troublesome. The engine ran well after the 1921 work, the flywheel being very good after the modification. The mill was closed about 1960, and all scrapped. Originally there were 4 boilers by Fernihough working at 85 psi, and all Corliss valves.

123) Stalybridge, John Summers & Co., Nail Works   SER 1226

Type:	Horizontal single tandem condensing
Photo taken:	1966
Maker and Date:	Scott and Hodgson, Guide Bridge, 1890s?
Cylinder/dimensions:	16in and 30in x 3ft 6in – Corliss and piston valves
Hp: 3-400	*Rpm:* 80 *Psi:* 120
Service:	Rolling mill drive. Rolling mill shaft coupled direct

The history of this was unknown, but it was probably made for Summers, by Scott and Hodgsons, who made several engines for them. It was said to have been bought from an exhibition and altered for J. Summers, but this is unlikely. It drove rolling mills which rolled sections of scrapped boiler shell to thin flats 4in x ^{1}/$_8$in thick for making cut nails largely for export to the Central African market. There was a good supply of boiler shell sections from the scrap dealers, and the mill was generally busy. However, the trade did die off, and metal was in short supply, and the whole plant was scrapped about 1966. There had also been a rope drive to the pulley at the opposite end of the engine room, latterly disused. There had been a large nail making section in these works and two other engines scrapped.

124) Stockport, Gorsey Bank Doubling Co., Cheadle Heath   SER 1122

Type:	Horizontal single tandem
Photo taken:	1963
Maker and Date:	J & E Wood, Bolton, 1908
Cylinder/dimensions:	17$^{1}/_{2}$in and 34in x 4ft 0in – Corliss valves
Hp: 300	*Rpm:* 60 *Psi:* 120
Service:	Cotton doubling to improve the yarn quality
	Later was condenser spinning

The site was very old in the cotton trade; and saw several changes over the years, and the engine was probably installed when doubling was started. There was almost certainly a beam engine once. Cotton doubling ceased about 1934, and the mill was re-opened for condenser spinning, probably working up poor quality cotton in 1939. It continued thus, and passed into the Fine Cotton Spinners group, and then the Lancashire Cotton Corporation, and finally closed in the later 1960s. All was scrapped. The engines had served with Fine Spinners for 39 years, 25 of them at Gorsey Bank.

125) Stockport, Kingston Mill   SER 1056

Type:	Mill interior. No machinery
Photo taken:	1961
Service:	Was cotton spinning, later storage

This was the Orrells Mill, a masterpiece of early mill design by William Fairbairn in the 1820s. The original power was a double beam engine with gear drive to an extensive weaving section on the lower part with a complete spinning plant in the remainder. It was thus a complete cotton cloth plant, finishing to the un-dyed stage. A village was also built for the workers since there was no housing nearby for them. The photograph is of the weaving shed portion at the rear of the spinning mill, the wall of which is seen at the left hand side, the weaving shed also occupying the ground floor under the mill; there was also a small weaving section at the side with a further seven shafts, apparently for loom drives, in addition to the 26in the main shed. A Yates & Thom engine of some 1,800 hp was also installed to drive the whole later. There were several changes of ownership, and cotton spinning ceased in the 1950s. There was a fine chimney on a hill away from the mill.

126) Stockport, Portwood Spinning Co.,   SER 886

Type:	Horizontal cross compound
Photo taken:	1957
Maker and Date:	George Saxon, Openshaw, date unknown
Cylinder/dimensions:	18in and 32in x 5ft 0in – Corliss valves
Hp: 600	*Rpm:* 61 *Psi:* 100
Service:	Cotton spinning. Geared drive

Portwood comprised several mill blocks, of 8-6-5- floors high, all at one time with geared drives, and probably beam engines in several. Horizontal engines replaced some of these with many of the gear drives retained, and in 1956 there were about 55 pairs of bevel wheels still in use. The gearing was very heavy, yet there seemed to be little power loss, as the spinning load was great for the power of the engines. Motor driving of various parts was continued, but the mills were finally closed about 1960. This engine was probably installed in the 1920s, but the latest one, a Hick, Hargreaves of similar type, of 1,050 h.p., installed in the late 1920s, had been replaced by motor drives by 1956. The whole of the plant was scrapped at the closure.

127) Stockport, Sykes & Co., Edgeley Bleach Works SER 1333

Type:	Horizontal single cylinder
Photo taken:	1968
Maker and Date:	Unknown
Cylinder/dimensions:	15in x 2ft 6in – Slide valve
Hp: about 20	*Rpm:* 80 *Psi:* 60
Service:	Water supply for bleaching. Geared $4^1/_2$ to 1 to two-throw well pumps

This was the main water supply for over 75 years, and was superseded by electric submerged pump in the 1950s. The well was 100ft deep, with a borehole 500ft deep below it. It remained unaltered structurally, despite the constant use, and the works completely depend upon the fresh water supply for washing out the bleach. The simple design, with four-bar crosshead guides, cast iron disc crank, heavy gearing and the fine cast iron pump crankshaft, with four stiffening ribs cast on it, and the two crank throws cast in one with it, were pure late mid-Victorian design at its best. It was retained in position, and would be well worth preserving as almost certainly the last example of such simple but sound industrial design.

128) Wallasey, Wallasey Dock Impounding Station SER 469

Type:	Three inverted vertical tandem condensing
Photo taken:	1952
Maker and Date:	J. & H. Gwynne & Co., Hammersmith, 1889
Cylinder/dimensions:	22in & 42in x 2ft 6in – Slide valves
Hp: 475 each	*Rpm:* 90 *Psi:* 120
Service:	Filling dock. Centrifugal pumps

These fulfilled various duties in the dock, and making good the water lost in locking vessels in low tides etc. The pumps were 54in pipe size, and could each move 900,000 gallons per minute against 18 - 21ft. head. By 1900 the load had grown, and the Allen triple expansion engine seen nearest to the camera was added, which of 800 h.p., increased the total capacity to 4,000,000 gallons per minute, but all were not used together. The whole was in use until 1970.

129) Wallasey, Wallasey Waterworks, Seaview Road SER 185

Type:	2 Woolf compound beam
Photo taken:	1937
Maker and Date:	Fawcett, Preston & Co., Liverpool, 1894
Cylinder/dimensions:	24in x 4ft 11in; 35in x 6ft 0in – Slide valves
Service:	Town supply from wells. 1 bucket and plunger pump 25in bucket – 18in ram 160ft down well and head of 100ft to reservoirs. 1,440,000 gallons per day each Beams 24ft long. Flywheel 21ft diameter

These were in constant use for over 30 years, but later a tandem horizontal engine, by the same makers, was more used because of its higher capacity. The beam engines were heavily made, with stiff fluted columns. Interesting features were the circular flywheel arms, each with 4 shallow ribs, the marine-type connecting rod ends, the wooden rods to the pumps, and the trunk guide for the top of the pump rod.

The No. 3 engine was horizontal tandem with slide valve cylinders about 30in & 60in bore x 5ft 0in stroke – 1902.

FAWCETT PRESTON & Cº LTD
1894
ENGINEERS LIVERPOOL

130) *Wilmslow, Stockport Waterworks, Wilmslow Pumping Station*
SER 1027a

Type:	Horizontal single tandem condensing
Photo taken:	1960
Maker and Date:	Marshall Sons & Co., Gainsborough, 1895
Cylinder/dimensions:	About 10in and 15in x 1ft 9in – Drop and Corliss valves
Hp: abt 50	*Rpm:* 80 *Psi:* 120
Service:	Town supply from well

An extremely neat little plant, with separate units for the well and the forcing service to the town reservoirs. The steam cylinders were fitted with the Proell-type of drop cutoff valves, with semi-rotary exhaust valves at the bottom. The condenser was at the back and driven from the piston tail rod. A cast iron disc crank and trunk guides, were usual Marshalls engine details, but the valve gear is the type Marshalls used before they settled to the top and bottom drop valves for steam and exhaust. A new borehole and pumping system was installed in 1960, and all of the steam plant and buildings were scrapped. There were two boilers by Tinker, Shenton – 1921. The force pumps are on the right (see SER 1027b).

131) *Wilmslow, Stockport Waterworks, Wilmslow Pumping Station*
SER 1027b

Type:	Inverted vertical compound rotative pumps
Photo taken:	1960
Maker and Date:	F. Pearn & Co., Manchester, 1895
Cylinder/dimensions:	Tandems = 9in and 15in x 1ft 0in
	Cross compound = 12in and 21in x 1ft 3in
Hp: ?	*Rpm:* 25 *Psi:* 120
Service:	Surface force pumps to reservoirs. Double-acting ram pumps

The surface lift pumps were large for the Pearn rotative type; the cross compound (nearest in the print) was 10ft. high, and the tandems were nearly 17ft. to the top. No details of the duties were available, but they were extremely quiet and with the compound expansion quite economical for a small works. The whole plant was extremely well kept, highly efficient and a credit to all concerned and was a type not often met.

Shropshire

132) *Bridgnorth, Pendlestone Mill*
SER 544

Type:	Vertical single cylinder condensing
Photo taken:	1953
Maker & Date:	Wood Bros., Sowerby Bridge, 1866
Cylinder/dimensions:	27in x 3ft 6in – Slide valve
Hp: 25	*Rpm:* 60 *Psi:* 60
Service:	Originally cotton mill

This was said to have been suplied when Wolverhampton Corporation acquired the water rights of the wheel which drove the mill until then. It was certainly made by Woods, and with the exception of a new cylinder to replace a cracked one in 1903 seems to have needed little attention until the mill closed in the early 1930s; the original boiler was replaced at the same time as the cylinder. It was housed in an extension of the mill at the opposite end to the water turbine, put in in the 1880s possibly to use any available water power. The parallel motion guiding the crosshead wss usual with the Yorkshire vertical engines, which were little used outside of the county for mill drives.

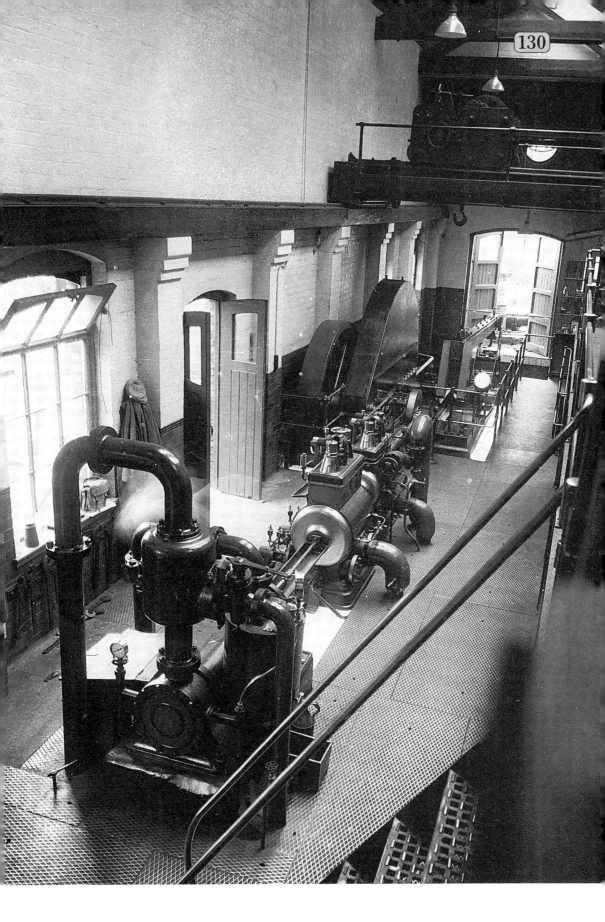

133) Broseley, Prestage & Broseley Tileries, Deep Pit Clay Mine   SER 54

Type:	Single rotative beam condensing
Photo taken:	1936
Maker & Date:	Broseley Foundry?, 1800?
Cylinder/dimensions:	15in x 3ft 0in – Slide valve
Hp: 20-25	*Rpm:* 20 *Psi:* 10-12
Service:	Wound clay from pit 100yds deep, 12 cwt of clay per trip
	Beam 12ft 0in long. Flywheel 10ft 0in diameter

Very early engine of simplest construction. The pit was known to be at work in 1800, and the owners were satisfied that it was the original engine; there was no record of a change. The only known repair was a piston rod replacement in 1930. The slide valve was operated by bumpers on the plug rod, a very early feature, and the engine was reversed to lower the clay wagons into the Deep pit which had reached 100 yds by 1937. The gears were 14in pinion to a gear 5ft 6in on the drum shaft; the drum was 6ft 6in diameter. The winding trip took about three minutes, but the incline was steep. It was worked by one man, who fired the small amount of coal used by the egg-ended boiler which was 4ft 6in diameter x 24ft long. The engine frame was of timber. The clay pit closed in 1941.

134) Bucknell, Mr R. M. Woolley   SER 686

Type:	Compound cable ploughing – Russian type
Photo taken:	1954
Maker & Date:	John Fowler and Co., Leeds, No 14982
Service:	Land ploughing

This was a special type developed for export. The special feature was that the ploughing drum was driven by a diagonal shaft to an angle wheel drive and spur gear reduction to the cable drum, which was smaller than usual. The design was specially produced for the Russian Government about 1915, but not delivered owing to the political conditions. This one may have been preserved, but the bottom of the firebox was damaged by frost, and it was probably cut up for scrap.

135) Eardington, Daniel's Flour Mill   SER 799

Type:	High breast waterwheel
Photo taken:	1956
Maker & Date:	Unknown
Cylinder/dimensions:	About 38ft diameter x 2ft 6in wide
Hp:	*Rpm:* *Psi:* No other data
Service:	Mill drive. Single pinion drive off gear ring

This was unusual in that it was rare to take the drive from the arms of a light tension bucket wheel of this type. It was customary to take the drive by a toothed ring at the rim of the wheel, so relieving the arms of the driving stresses. The whole did suggest that water was originally from a much lower source, and that latterly a high stream was secured and the greatly enlarged diameter was then adopted. The increased area of the wheel arms where the gear ring was attached suggested that it was so re-arranged, to use the higher head but still drive from the original pinion and mill shaft. It was in use in the 1950s.

136) Ellesmere, Shropshire Union Canal Co., Workshop   SER 467

Type:	Table engine non condensing
Photo taken:	1952
Maker & Date:	Unknown, c. 1850s?
Cylinder/dimensions:	9in x 1ft 6in – Slide valve
Hp: 8-10	*Rpm:* 45 *Psi:* 60
Service:	Plant drive

This mainly drove a vertical frame-saw for cutting planking, and was as simple as possible. The globular crosshead, and curved guide framing, and half cranks were unusual on table engines. The drive for the slide valve was very uncommon in being taken from the engine crankpin horizontally, and then by a right angle lever to the vertical valve spindle, the only one I met so arranged. The general plain form suggested Midlands design. The crosshead ran in vee shaped surfaces (they were usually flat blocks).

137) Hadnall, Mr F. Dowley, Seven Gables (Scrap dealer)   SER 434

Type:	Compound traction engine
Photo taken:	1952
Maker & Date:	E Foden & Co., Sandbach, No 411
Cylinder/dimensions:	7in and 10in x 1ft 0in – Slide valve
Hp: ?	*Rpm:* 140 *Psi:* 220
Service:	Machinery dealers yard. Disused

Standard Foden design, history not known. It was completed, with the long valve chests, the rear wheel with many spokes and two speed gear. It was probably cut up as scrap metal about 1954. This also applies to the Foster single cylinder No 12,908, and Aveling and Porter tandem roller on the site at the time.

138) Lee Brockhurst, Mr Neate, The Farm   SER 466

Type:	Compound farm tractor
Photo taken:	1952
Maker & Date:	Mann's Patent Steam Cart & Wagon Co,. Leeds, 1914, No 1426
Cylinder/dimensions:	4in and 6³/₈in x 8in – Slide valves
Hp: ?	*Rpm:* 140? *Psi:* 150
Service:	Farm work

This was unsprung, with all gear drive, and was used largely for breaking clods of heavy soil in later years. There were three speeds, and the engine was very compact with the valves between the cylinders. The usual Mann single eccentric reversing gear was fitted and there was a governor for control when threshing. There were 29 tubes in the boiler, which was still sound when scrapped in the 1950s.

139) Madeley, Ironbridge Gorge Museum Trust, Blists Hill site   SER 1440a1

Type:	Double cylinder condensing beam – *David & Sampson*
Photo taken:	1972
Maker & Date:	Murdoch, Aitken and Co., Glasgow, 1851
Cylinder/dimensions:	$38^3/_4$in x 7ft 10in stroke – Cornish valves
Hp: 269 max	*Rpm:* 12 *Psi:* 42
Service:	Blast furnace blower. Two air cylinders – 78in x 7ft 10in up to 20,000 cubic feet per minute to 4 psi

This plant was installed to blow the then New Furnaces of the Lilleshall Co., which ran their first cast of metal on Christmas Eve 1851. They were in constant use for some fifty years, possibly with the single cylinder engine SER 1440b as a standby. With major alterations around 1900, new furnaces and American type blowing engines made by the Lilleshall Co. were then installed which took the blowing load until ironmaking ceased at the site in 1959. The beam engines were however available as standby engines until 1952, when they were disconnected. All of the plant was dismantled, after iron making ceased, but the beam engines were saved, and latterly moved to Blists Hill. This was a major project which has saved these, and SER 1440b, probably the only examples of Victorian furnace blowers to survive. The steam cylinders are those near to the cranks, the whole being in the open air but with a roof overhead.

140) Madeley, Ironbridge Gorge Museum Trust, Blists Hill site   SER 1440a2

Type:	Horn type sway beam. 30ft overall length
Photo taken:	1972
Service:	Blast furnace blowers. Steam end

Rotative beam blowing engines were often designed with the steam and the air cylinders of equal stroke, but opposite sides of the beam centre. The connecting rod was worked from the end of the beam, which was often swept upwards to form the horn end seen in the print, and the crankshaft, beyond the steam cylinder, gave a longer stroke for the crank, than to either of the cylinders. The upswept horn can be seen in the print, as, beneath the flooring, can be seen the ornamental brackets for the steam end parallel motion. Although extensively used for early beam blowing engines, this "horn" end was scarcely ever used for any other service. The blowing connecting rods were often made of timber for flexibility, as can be seen in the example. There appears to be little advantage in the horn end design.

141) Madeley, Ironbridge Gorge Museum Trust, Blists Hill site   SER 1440b1

Type:	Inverted vertical single cylinder
Photo taken:	1972
Maker & Date:	Possibly Lilleshall Co., 1880's?
Cylinder/dimensions:	33in x 4ft 0in – Slide valve
Hp: 103	*Rpm:* 20 *Psi:* 40-60
Service:	Blast furnace blower. Air cylinder abt 72in x 4ft 0in

A typical sound ironworks engine it was non-condensing and entirely without ornament, or anything that could be done without. The flywheel is extremely heavy, 16ft 6in diameter with rim of 13in x 19in section, and made entirely without fitted joints, i.e. all the arms are fitted into the rim by dovetails with large clearances, which are filled with wooden packing strips tightened with steel wedges. It is constructed of the smallest number of parts, i.e. the side frames are each a single casting, as is the bed, with the air blowing "tub" directly on the columns, with a single piston rod from the steam cylinder on the top, to the blowing tub piston, and the crosshead. It is preserved, a good example of simple reliable designing.

142) Madeley, Ironbridge Gorge Museum Trust, Blists Hill site   SER 1440b2

Type:	Inverted vertical single cylinder
Photo taken:	1972
Maker & Date:	Possibly Lilleshall Co., 1880s?
Cylinder/dimensions:	33in x 4ft 0in – Slide valve
Hp: 103	*Rpm:* 20 *Psi:* 40-60
Service:	Blast furnace blower. Air blowing cylinder 72in x 4ft 0in – 4,500 cubic feet per minute to $4^{1}/_{2}$ psi

No history of this engine survives, but it was probably made by the Lilleshall Co. as a standby engine to the beam blowers SER 1440a which were regularly used until 1900. It is a typical heavy blowing engine, very massive and plain, and appears never to have been condensing, and with nothing superfluous. The air valves on the blowing cylinder were automatically operated, and were in a cluster around the cylinder, which can be seen at the top of the photograph. The pipe coming from this was the delivery to the blast furnace. The whole was completely utility designed, massive and with virtually nothing to go wrong. This is preserved on the same site as the beam engine SER 1440a. The capacity is about one-third of the beam engines, a limitation which prevented it from taking the full capacity if the beams failed, but it would save serious damage to the furnaces if they did. Blists Hill thus represents a good example of Victorian blowing practice.

143) Oakengates, Lilleshall Co. Ironworks   SER 965a

Type:	Horizontal twin cylinder non-condensing
Photo taken:	1959
Maker & Date:	Possibly Lilleshall Co., late 19th Century
Cylinder/dimensions:	32in x 4ft 0in – Slide valves
Hp: 1200 max	*Rpm:* 120 *Psi:* 100
Service:	Steel rolls drive. Direct coupled

This was probably made for the mill by Lilleshall Co. This was the only steel rolling unit at the works which with five or six blast furnaces made mostly pig iron. There were twelve blast furnace gas fired boilers which ran the blast furnace blowing engines. It was a very plain engine, which had given very little trouble beyond the usual heavy steel load wear, but tail piston rod supports were added about 1912, and a spare crankshaft made by Somers of Halesowen, Staffs in 1918, was fitted some 34 years later. Steel rolling was continued after the blast furnaces were shut down in 1959, but it was not economical and the entire works was dismantled in the 1960s. There were two fine beam blowing engines of 1851, (see SER 1440a1), which are now preserved at Ironbridge, but these had been superseded by a large inverted vertical compound set made in the works in 1903. There was also a single inverted vertical which is also preserved at Ironbridge, and these are the only blowing engines preserved in the U.K, where pig iron making has largely ceased.

144) Oakengates, Lilleshall Co., Colliery, Priors Lee   SER 55

Type:	Single rotative beam
Photo taken:	1936
Maker & Date:	Lilleshall Co.,? 1830 on beam
Cylinder/dimensions:	36in x 6ft 0in – Drop valves
Hp: ?	*Rpm:* 20 *Psi:* 30
Service:	Coal shaft winder, later men only. Drum 11ft 0in diameter
	Gears 4ft & 7ft 6in
	Beam 18ft 0in long. Flywheel 15ft 0in diameter

The brick house and general structure were typical of early local design and almost certainly had remained unaltered. It was one of the early pits of the area; little was known of its history but it was considered to be a Lilleshall Co., enterprise.

145) Oakengates, Lilleshall Co., Stafford Pit   SER 250a

Type:	Bull Engine
Photo taken:	1938
Maker & Date:	Lilleshall Co.,? c. 1850?
Cylinder/dimensions:	36in x 6ft 0in – Drop valves
Hp: ?	*Spm: 5-6* *Psi: 25*
Service:	Colliery second shaft pump. Shaft 120yds deep
	Pump data unknown

This was not a pure Bull engine since there were only two valves, so that there was no equilibrium stroke, but the upper part of the piston was permanently open to the exhaust by a trunk at the side of the cylinder. The pump rods were simply lifted by the steam below the piston, and there was no condenser.

146) Oakengates, Lilleshall Co., Stafford Pit   SER 250b

Type:	Single rotative beam
Photo taken:	1938
Maker & Date:	Lilleshall Co.,? 1850?
Cylinder/dimensions:	36in x 6ft 0in – Drop valves
Hp: ?	*Rpm: 20* *Psi: 25*
Service:	Second shaft winding engine
	Flywheel 18ft 0in diameter

Possibly due to trouble with water, these two engines ran non-condensing, although they had almost certainly been designed for condensing. There was no expansion on this engine as the steam and exhaust valves were driven from the same shaft, and worked by fixed cams.

147) Shrewsbury, Coleham Head Sewage Pumping Station   SER 249

Type:	2 Woolf compound beam
Photo taken:	1938
Maker & Date:	W R Renshaw, Stoke-on-Trent, 1897
Cylinder/dimensions:	16in x 3ft 6in – Slide valves
	24in x 4ft 6in – Drop valves
Service:	Pump to sewage farm. 2 plunger pumps off beam
	2 million gallons per day – 35ft head
	Beam 15ft long. Flywheel 14ft diameter

The entire town drainage depended upon these two engines for over 70 years, and they stopped work in 1970. One was always at work, it speeds down sometimes to 8 rpm, since the sewer storage was limited, and flooding soon occured. In view of this the other engine was always in steam ready for any heavy demand. The use of slide valves on the hp, with drop valves on the low pressure is unusual. The hp Meyer cut-off valve was driven from a pin near the beam centre, and the main valve from an eccentric on the side shaft. Steam was supplied by 2 Cornish boilers at 75 psi, with underfeed stokers, but only one was used at a time.

ENGINE MAKERS INDEX

Company	SER	Plate
Adamson, D., & Co.,	947	19
	940a	52
	656	98
	808	107
	605	113
	728	119
Armstrong, WG	819	33
Armstrong, Whitworth	1328	111
Ashby, Jeffery & Luke,	653b	10
Barclay, A., & Sons	1317a	20
	1317b	21
	680a	82
	259	100
Barker & Cope	1312a	61
Bridgwater Trust	98	118
British Thompson Houston	1327b	24
Broseley Foundry	54	133
Carels Frères	640	117
Clarke, Chapman & Co.,	1305	69
Cole, Marchent & Morley	940b	53
	945a	56
	811	88
Daglish & Co	685	92
Davy Brothers	1118	22
De Winton	653a	9
	654	12
Fawcett, Preston & Co	185	129
Foden, E	943	15
	1167	106
Forrester, George, & Co.,	101	99
Fowler, John, & Co	682	29
	959a	65
Fraser & Chalmers	679	50
Fullerton, Hodgart & Barclay	1321a	74
Galloways Ltd.,	850	16
	934	18
	944	45
	945	47
	1301a	48
	400	58
	402b	84
	402c	85

Company	SER	Plate
	815c	87
	852	91
	853	93
Goodfellow, B, & Co.,	638	109
	606b	112
	877	122
Gwynne, J &H., & Co	469	128
Harvey & Co	847a	94
	847b	95
	847c	96
	258	102
Hawthorn Davey & Co.,	1497	76
Hick, Hargreaves & Co.,	941	17
	963	37
	850c	57
	850d	72
	961	90
Holman Brothers	653	8
Hydraulic Engineering Co.,	819	33
Lamberton & Co.,	948	51
Leigh, J D	1313b	68
Leigh, J & W	1307	70
Lilleshall Co.,	1003	103
	1440b1	141
	1440b2	142
	965a	143
	55	144
	250a	145
	250b	146
Llewellyn & Cubitt	1310b	44
Marshall, Sons & Co.,	1027a	130
Markham & Co.,	1327a	23
	1316b	41
	1319a	78
	1319b	79
Mather (?Liverpool)	1413	11
Murdoch, Aitken & Co.,	1440a1	139
Musgrave J., & Sons Ltd.,	942	59
	962	64
	815a	86
Naysmith, Wilson & Cp.,	684	81
Neath Abbey Ironworks	812	89
Newbridge Foundry	1314	60
Pearn, F, & Co.,	1027b	131
Qualter Hall & Co.,	1316c	42
Renshaw, W R.,	249	147
Richardson	955	32
Robey & Co.,	1321b	75

Company	SER	Plate
Saxon, George, Ltd.,	494	105
	886	126
Scott & Hodgson	688	28
	949	62
	1142	108
	714	110
	877	122
	1226	123
Soudley Foundry	683	36
Summers and Scott	810	35
Thornewill & Warham	681	30
	1310	38
	680b	83
Union Engineering Co.,	1313a	67
Unknown	1442	26
	1441	27
	1309	31
	1302	39
	1310a	43
	1318	46
	1306	71
	85a	73
	1189a	114
	1333	127
	467	136
	1440a2	140
Uskside Engineering Co.,	1315	54
Waddle Patent Fan & Eng. Co.,	1304b	55
Wainwright, T & Sons	897	120
	690	121
Walker Brothers	1319c	80
	847d	97
Westinghouse, USA	468	101
Whitaker & Low	1320	77
Wood Brothers	851	63
	544	132
Wood, J & E	1122	124
Worsley Mesnes Ltd.,	1316	40
	959c	66

Type	SER	Plate
Fowler Ploughing Engines	689	116
	686	134
Locomotives	652a	1
	687a	4
	687c	5
	655 (2)	6
	655 (8)	7
	651	13
Mill Interior	1056	125
Traction Engines	434	137
	466	138
Water Balance Hoists	652b	2
	683	36
Water wheels		
Dinorwic Quarry	687	3
Abergwili	964	14
Rossett	471	25
Melingriffith	820	34
Bollington	257	104
Kettleshulme	1189b	115
Eardington	799	135
Yorkshire Boilers	1301b	49

SERIES EDITOR, TONY WOOLRICH

Tony was born in Bristol in 1938. He became interested in technical history in his school days, and has been a Member of the Newcomen Society for 40 years, for ten years of which serving as a sub-editor of the *Newcomen Transactions*. He is also a Member of SHOT (the Society for the History of Technology), ICOHTEC (the International Committee for the History of Technology) and the Somerset Archaeological and Natural History Society.

He trained as a craftsman in the engineering industry, and from 1970 has combined his craft and historical skills in modelmaking for museums and heritage projects.

He has also published books and articles on aspects of technical history and biography. A particular interest is industrial espionage of the 18th century. Another interest is 18th century and early 19th century technical books and encyclopaedias, in particular Rees's *Cyclopædia*, (1802-1819). He has been working on a biography of the engineer John Farey, jr (1791-1851) for the past 20 years.

Since 1989 he has been heavily involved cataloguing for the National Monuments Record, Swindon, the Watkins Collection on the Stationary Steam Engine. He is also a constant consultee to the Monuments Protection Programme of English Heritage.

Since 1994 he has been acting as a contributor to the New *Dictionary of National Biography* working on biographies of engineers and industrialists. He is a contributor to the *Biographical Dictionary of Civil Engineers*, published by the Institution of Civil Engineers, 2002

He has recently completed for Wessex Water plc a study of the water supplies of Bridgwater, Wellington (Somerset) and Taunton, and was part of the team setting up the company's education centres at Ashford (near Bridgwater) and Sutton Poyntz (near Weymouth).

ACKNOWLEDGEMENTS

Thanks are due to Keith Falconer who had the foresight to acquire the collection for the RCHME, and to Helga Lane, (late of the RCHME Salisbury office) who made the original computer database of the Steam Engine Record.

Much help in the production of these volumes has been given by David Birks, National Monuments Record Archives Administration Officer; Anna Eavis, Head of Enquiry and Research Services, and the members of the public search room staff at Swindon.

Colin Bowden and Jane Woolrich did the often-difficult proof checking.

Many thanks to John Cornwell for providing the photographs of the author.

Bryan Davies and Dr Ivor Brown read George Watkins original notes, on Wales and Shropshire respectively and made useful comments. A few of these, concerning spelling corrections, have been incorporated into the texts printed here, but the remainder, dealing with the present state of the sites, will be used when compiling the corrections to the series, to be published in volume 10.

The series publishes George Watkins's texts as he wrote them and it is acknowledged that he did make mistakes. While obvious spelling and typing errors have been changed, to begin to rewrite his work in the light of present-day knowledge is an impossible task.

The Publisher and Editor welcome constructive comments from readers. Where appropriate, these will be incorporated into volume 10.

LANDMARK COLLECTOR'S LIBRARY

LANDMARK COLLECTOR'S LIBRARY

STATIONARY STEAM ENGINES OF GREAT BRITAIN

THE NATIONAL PHOTOGRAPHIC COLLECTION

VOLUME 5: THE NORTH MIDLANDS

Derbyshire, Leicestershire, Lincolnshire, Nottinghamshire & Staffordshire

George Watkins

LANDMARK COLLECTOR'S LIBRARY

Mining Histories

- Collieries of South Wales: Vol 1 *ISBN: 1 84306 015 9, £22.50*
- Collieries of South Wales: Vol 2 *ISBN: 1 84306 017 5, £19.95*
- Collieries of Somerset & Bristol *ISBN: 1 84306 029 9, £14.95*
- Copper & Lead Mines around the Manifold Valley, North Staffordshire *ISBN: 1 901522 77 6, £19.95*
- Images of Cornish Tin *ISBN: 1 84306 020 5, £29.95*
- Lathkill Dale, Derbyshire, its Mines and Miners *ISBN: 1 901522 80 6, £8.00*
- Rocks & Scenery the Peak District *ISBN: 1 84306 026 4, paperback, £7.95, May 02*
- Swaledale, its Mines & Smelt Mills *ISBN: 1 84306 018 3, £19.95*

Industrial Histories

- Alldays and Onions *ISBN: 1 84306 047 7, £24.95, July 02*
- The Life & Inventions of Richard Roberts, 1789 -1864 *ISBN: 1 84306 027 2, £29.95, May 02*
- The Textile Mill Engine *ISBN: 1 901522 43 1, paperback, £22.50*
- Watt, James, His Life in Scotland, 1736-74 *ISBN 1 84306 045 0, £29.95. May 02*
- Wolseley, The Real, Adderley Park Works, 1901-1926 *ISBN 1 84306 052 3, £16.95 approx, July 02*
- Morris Commercial *ISBN: 1 84306 069 8 (Price to be announced)*

Roads & Transportantion

- Packmen, Carriers & Packhorse Roads *ISBN: 1 84306 016 7, £19.95*
- Roads & Trackways of Wales *ISBN: 1 84306 019 1, £22.50*
- Welsh Cattle Drovers *ISBN: 1 84306 021 3, £22.50*
- Peakland Roads & Trackways *ISBN: 1 901522 91 1, £19.95*

Regional/Local Histories

- Colwyn Bay, Its History across the Years *ISBN: 1 84306 014 0, £24.95*
- Crosses of the Peak District *ISBN 1 84306 044 2, £14.95*
- Derbyshire Country Houses: Vol 1 *ISBN: 1 84306 007 8, £19.95*
- Derbyshire Country Houses: Vol 2 *ISBN: 1 84306 041 8, £19.95*
- Historic Hallamshire *ISBN: 1 84306 049 3, £19.95*
- Llandudno: Queen of Welsh Resorts *ISBN 1 84306 048 5, paperback, £9.95*
- Lost Houses in and around Wrexham *ISBN 1 84306 057 4, £16.95*
- Lost Houses of Derbyshire *ISBN: 1 84306 064 7, £19.95, October 02*
- Shipwrecks of North Wales *ISBN: 1 84306 005 1, £19.95*
- Well Dressing *ISBN: 1 84306 042 6, £19.95*

Full details upon request

LANDMARK
Publishing Ltd ● ● ● ●

Ashbourne Hall, Cokayne Ave, Ashbourne, Derbyshire, DE6 1EJ England
Tel 01335 347349 Fax 01335 347303
e-mail landmark@clara.net web site: www.landmarkpublishing.co.uk